D0514694

THE DASTARDLY DUCHESS
AND
THE DOOMED DOMESTIC

Nancy. L. Mangan

Published by: Nancy. L. Mangan 2019

First edition: 30 August 2019

Prologue

Recent Work Experience

Housekeeper (domestic servant) at Cauldron Manor, somewhere in the Highlands, somewhere in Scotland, sometime in the 21st century with the option to time travel back to the 18th century.

Duties:

- Vacuum cleaning miles of threadbare but priceless carpets
- Specialised vacuum cleaning ancient, handmade silk rugs
- Cleaning, polishing and dusting thousands of ornaments and old furniture
- Polishing miles of ancient grimy wooden floors (on hands and knees)
- Removing mouldy black bits from hundreds of rotting frames around countless, small-paned cobweb covered windows
- Making beds with old linen sheets using hospital corners then ironing said sheets, pillowcases and duvet covers while on the bed.
- Cleaning bathrooms and polishing copper and brass bathroom fittings over baths big enough to house a family

- Filling water carafes with filtered water from a tap in a kitchen hundreds of miles from the bedrooms and NOT from the tap in a hand basin in the nearest bathroom.
- Paying close attention to detail of... not quite sure
- Tolerating verbal abuse for minor infractions usually the result of not paying close enough attention to detail

Skills learnt:
How to:
- Survive in a medieval workplace
- Clean ancient artefacts
- Polish Victorian brass and copper bath fittings... endlessly
- Use expensive toothpaste to remove the black stuff from brass and copper, and porcelain -without getting caught
- Mix vinegar and salt to clean ancient toilets, baths, and basins
- Understand the crucial importance of different towel sizes
- Identify the correct lemon size and colour for the bedside tray
- Observe, surreptitiously, the machinations of scheming, narcissistic staff members
- Smile bravely when crying hysterically inside

APRIL

Cauldron Manor is the manorial home of one of those famous (infamous?) Scottish families clinging like crazy to their ancestral advantages which appear to consist largely of 'I was born with a title' and/or 'I inherited shed loads of money and/or an ancestral pile (possibly several)' therefore, I am better than you.

Not criticising, just commenting.

I am offered and accept a temporary job as a housekeeper for the summer season. It is a welcome opportunity after an extended period of unemployment (true, most of it was spent swanning around India and Morocco but unemployed nonetheless), despite the minimum hourly wage and small number of hours. Still, after more years than I care to remember running my own business, I relish the thought of simply going to work, doing my job, heading home when I finish and not thinking about work until the next day. The mere thought fills me with joy.

Ah, bliss.

Monday 24th

My first day.

I'm excited walking up the long driveway from the car park where the overhanging, ancient looking trees coming into leaf are that lovely, light spring yellow-green. I punch a number into a clocking-on machine which greets me with a staccato American voice. This allows employees to get through the gates leading to the circular drive way which swoops around in the of the Manor's entrance. This bit of modern monitoring does jar a little but I let it pass as the sun is shining, it's almost warm, and I'm having a bit of a 'gosh moment' to think I'm actually working in this amazingly ancient place.

Cauldron Manor is an interesting mix of a castle and a manor house - I've done my research. Where would we be without Professor Google? – when the first part was built early in the 12th century. It's been added onto in an interesting and chaotically higgledy-piggledy manner over the subsequent centuries. I'm not sure if it's intentional but it certainly gives the whole edifice an unusual and rather unique flavour. The Manor is still in the family, so to speak, as the late Duke's second wife, the Dowager Duchess is in residence though I understand the National Trust has been sniffing around it for a few years.

There are also some astonishing, though undoubtedly made up (I hope) legends attached to the place. Like the one where the Duke or Baron or Laird or whatever title he held at that time, chopped off the fingers of his errant daughter as she clung to a window ledge during her attempted elopement with some inappropriate lad from a neighbouring (enemy) clan, thereby causing her to fall into the freezing moat below.

Wow! The lad must have been really inappropriate as a son-in-law. I'm guessing she'd have died from her wounds otherwise life would be a bit difficult for a woman without fingers in a time when embroidery appears to be the only acceptable occupation for unwed daughters of the aristocracy.

I stop on the drawbridge with its black iron portcullis poised threateningly over the entrance to look down reflectively into what must have once been the moat but is now an ornate sunken garden. They both, the drawbridge with portcullis and moat, look more ornamental than serious and as I stare down, I try to image the moat full of fingerless, bloodied, eloping medieval maidens but my mind isn't imaginative enough. All I see is grass and flowering bushes though as I look up and scan the sheer grey stone walls, I think the daughter must have been very desperate to escape for her to have ever imagined climbing out any of the windows on view was a viable possibility. Even the lowest ones are a long way from the ground.

As I continue across the drawbridge, I notice a couple of men wearing blue overalls sweeping up leaves and debris. They stop and fold their hands on top of their broom handles where they rest their chins while watching me walk towards them.

Bit unnerving.

'Morning,' they say nodding while looking me up and down with a certain interest until I get close enough for them to clock I am no longer in the first flush of youth at which point their faces fall with disappointment.

'Morning,' I say, 'it's a beaut of a day isn't it?' I add beaming at them. Sometimes it pays to play up the antipodeanisms if there is such a word. If there isn't, I've just made it up.

'Oh aye, that it is,' one of them responds but I sense they've lost interest. I think it's the way they go back to sweeping and no longer look at me.

I make my way around to the back door where I find another housekeeper waiting. She looks pleased to see me.

'Hello, I'm Davina. Good to see you. We are so short staffed,' she explains crisply (well, I think it's what she says; her accent is a little difficult to follow and my ear is not yet attuned to it) as she leads me through a huge wooden heavily studded door - it looks positively medieval and for a nanosecond I feel a rush of excitement. What's on the other side? Narnia?

Sadly, the expectation promised by the fabulous door does not follow through. Inside it's dark and dreary with an unpleasant pervasive odour of toilet cleaner and bleach. Davina leads the way down a kind of ramp where the floor slopes down into what, I assume, must once have been the servants' passage before she stops in a room which is really nothing more than an uncomfortable cross between corridor and cupboard. This corridor/cupboard, it transpires, is the housekeepers' room where the cleaning equipment is kept along with loads of rubbish; empty boxes, broken ladders, rubbish bins and so on. It smells musty; of mould, old rubbish and vinegar.

Inside this gloomy corridor/cupboard, a large youngish woman is extracting a vacuum cleaner from one of the cupboards lining the wall. She appears to be hissing at another woman standing beside her. Davina introduces the hissing woman as Jodie, another housekeeper, and the other as Effie... Affie... Offie... or something like that but it could be anything because inside the corridor/cupboard's dead airlessness, Davina's accent makes it sound like she's speaking a foreign language.

Jodie glares belligerently, first at me, then at Davina and back to me again. In a novel, such a look would be described as 'baleful'. She comes across as very angry. Not sure why. I remind myself it's nothing to do with me. I am not the boss. Whatever is bothering her is not my problem. I take a slow breath.

'I do upstairs,' she snarls at me before I can speak. She plugs herself into her iPod and marches through the door at the opposite end of the corridor/cupboard pulling the vacuum cleaner behind her. I watch as she stops at the bottom of some stairs, turns on her iPod, picks up the vacuum cleaner and stomps up the stairs singing loudly and very out of tune.

Effie... Affie...Offie turns to Davina and says; 'I was just after getting ower hoover back. Can you no be helping yoursels to it all the fecking time? You've got your own for feck's sake and I'm sick of lugging it back down they fecking bloody steep stone stairs.'

Well, it's a loose interpretation but whatever, her tone isn't friendly. I don't know what to say so I say nothing. I am new. I know when to keep my mouth shut but I sense maybe all is not quite so lovely inside this lovely Manor.

Davina ignores her, shrugs, hauls another vacuum cleaner from the cupboard and tells me I am to do downstairs today while she does the dusting. I am, it seems, to vacuum the tartan carpet. I stare at her. Tartan carpet? She jerks her head and leads me through the door at the other end of the cupboard/corridor to show me a carpet about a metre-wide which snakes through the room. This, she tells me, is the family tartan and the carpet works like a path going through various rooms but only those open to the public. This carpet, it seems, indicates the route visitors take.

Apparently, if I follow the carpet, I will get to know the route. This is my new job: on the days I'm scheduled to work, I am to vacuum the carpet, which is pretty filthy as I suppose is only to be expected after a few hundred people have trekked their way through the house, and then I must do as much dusting as I can manage to get through before Cauldron Manor opens to the public. The parts open to the public are a mere minuscule percentage of the whole which is a shame. For me, it's always those rooms beyond the locked doors that always suggest more interesting space but, hey, maybe I'm just nosy.

Davina takes me through one room, opens the door and shows me how the carpet snakes off into another room but to the side, there are stone steps which also has a narrower version of the carpet on each step. This carpet route looks long and circuitous; I'm worried I might get lost. I've seen from the outside, the Manor appears to possess a surfeit of twisty towers and now on the inside, it appears they are all reached by ascending very worn stone stairs with only a rope strung along one wall to hang onto to prevent a headlong plunge onto the flagstones below.

Davina leads me back to the first room pointing out power sockets as she goes. Most, apparently don't work because the 'electric needs to be sorted'. I guess she means modernised.

'I'll do the dusting today,' she tells me, which is good because I'm feeling a bit daunted by it all. 'Because if you move any ornaments or photos a fraction of an inch, it sets off the alarms.' She throws this comment casually over her shoulder as she opens another large ancient looking, studded door and disappears into a darkened room beyond. For a second, I am alone and it's slightly scary. Then it hits me what she's just said.

Alarms? What? Really? For some reason, this makes me nervous. Not sure why. It's not as if I intend to move or steal anything but oddly the mere thought of alarms makes me feel guilty. Don't know why this surprises me, the place is ancient and full of probably priceless stuff. I'm surprised there aren't CCTV cameras everywhere.

'There are also the CCTV cameras,' Davina who is little and round, reappears and points out the monitors to me. I realise we are standing by the closed front door in a kind of vestibule next to a desk. I guess this is where visitors enter. At the moment, the monitors are dark and dead like TV screens. Then she turns them on and they flicker into life revealing a number of dark, gloomy rooms.

I'm having second thoughts about this job.

My heart sinks. Lovely. Every move watched. Every hesitation noted. I must remember to not scratch or adjust anything of a personal nature. Or pick my nose. Not that I do usually but sometimes you don't have the option.

'You'll be all right,' she insists grinning at me. 'Just don't take it seriously.'

Then an alarm buzzes loudly and piercingly. I'm a bit slow so don't immediately realise it's an alarm.

Davina sighs. 'Bloody ghosts keep moving ornaments and setting alarms off. Now I've got to find which one.' She disappears back into the dark room beyond the studded door.

Ghosts? Really?

Now I'm having third thoughts.

Seriously.

Where I'm standing it's very gloomy with many moving shadows. From upstairs, I hear the Jodie woman singing loudly and out of tune. A little flutter of icy air passes across my face. For a second I think someone's touched my cheek but no one's there.

I now know what rigid with shock feels like. It's not nice

Will anybody notice if I just walk out and leave? Will it matter if they did? Why do I care?

The alarm is silenced and Davina reappears.

'Right we better get moving,' she says.

Too late to run. I take a breath. A very deep one.

I ask if there's a lot to do. We have 2 hours to get through it all before the doors open to the public at 10.

'Aye, much too much. We rarely get through it,' she tells me rolling her eyes.

So much for a relaxing, stress-free job.

It is impressive, the Manor, well, the public rooms I get to see anyway. As I vacuum my way along the carpet, I'm overwhelmed by the weight of history creaking through the rooms. The walls are covered with ancient tapestries trapped for prosperity behind Perspex panels, the beds in all the bedrooms are four-posters ones big enough to house a small family and are high off the floor. I would need a step ladder to get up on one and while I'm not tall, I'm not exactly short either. The posts at each corner of every bed are intricately carved but dark and heavy looking. Not entirely sure I like them. Many of the canopies and curtains hanging from the posts are dark velvet and although they look pretty impressive from a distance, certainly from behind the rope barriers, closer inspection reveals moths have had a bit of a feast fest with them.

Davina tells me I'm not to touch the curtains but only dust the heavily embroidered bed covers. I suspect it's because the only thing holding the material together is dust.

I find out pretty quickly why they don't get through the allocated morning's work in time.

Gossip.

Davina and Jodie spend a considerable part of the morning resting their chins on their vacuum cleaner handles while gossiping and whispering. I feel I'm the only one actually doing any work but ... well, first day and all that... I decide to make a good impression and get on with it. Besides, it allows me to feel smug. Also, I'm a bit ashamed of my earlier moment of panic. I am made of tougher stuff.

At the end of the shift, Davina walks with me back to the car-park. It takes a long time as all other staff is beginning to arrive and I'm introduced to each one. This is kind but I am tired, their accents are thick and I can't remember a single name. I do note, however, there is an awful lot of eye rolling, teeth sucking and knowing-nodding going on.

I should pay attention but I want to get home and have a coffee.

Tuesday 25th

Today, many of those whom I met the previous day greet me by name. I'm a bit overwhelmed and slightly embarrassed because I can barely recall any of their names but, as I remind myself, they only have to remember one name, mine, whereas I have to remember a hundred ... well, slight exaggeration but it feels a little like it.

Today I meet Lucinda, one of the ticket collectors who sit at a desk by the front door greeting visitors in the gloomy vestibule along with the CCTV monitors. She's very thin, almost emaciated and has worked in the Manor every summer season since time began. Well, not exactly but I'm picking up there's not a lot she doesn't know about the comings and goings of the place.

'New management,' she says pointedly to Davina and they both roll their eyes.

'Again,' says Davina and they both roll their eyes again but add a little nod this time.

I'm guessing this 'new management' is a frequent occurrence and not a good thing.

Lucinda, I decide is probably as thin as she is because she uses an extraordinary amount of energy talking at great speed. In the space of approximately 5 minutes, I've heard all I ever want to hear about her daughters, sons, their husbands and wives and all their various children. Seriously, 5 minutes. I conclude she speaks using the same method as those who play the didgeridoo; by circular breathing. She can breathe in through her nose while simultaneously expelling stored words out of her mouth. In her presence, I feel all the oxygen around me being sucked out so I'm breathless being near her. I need to retreat to the Housekeepers' cupboard to gulp down some air, any air will do even if it does smell of old rubbish and vinegar.

I vacuum the upstairs today, which is the first time I've been up there so get lost briefly in the maze of rooms. It's all very well telling me to simply follow the carpet but the carpet doesn't seem to follow a route. It's also dark and a bit gloomy especially in the room labelled 'Long Gallery', with its many portraits of dark, gloomy and miserable looking people. Maybe they look like that because they were bored sitting so long while being painted or maybe their lives were just dark, gloomy and miserable.

I turn down a stone corridor. It's cold and feels damp. At the end is a door but when I try to open it, I find it's locked. I look down and discover I've strayed from the tartan carpet. I listen but can't hear Davina or Lucinda or anyone. The air around me feels thick and dead. I suddenly have a sense I'm being watched and worse, laughed at. It occurs to me, ghosts cansense panic. It's probably what gives them the energy to do their haunting thing.

Rubbish, I tell myself very firmly. Ghosts don't exist. Then I remember I do believe in ghosts. I take a steadying breath while I retrace my steps. It's a huge relief when I emerge from a room to find myself back on the landing from where I can hear Davina and Lucinda whispering downstairs. I spend a couple of minutes doing calm breathing to ground myself. I can only hope I've managed to vacuum all the carpet and not missed anywhere. I'm trying to pretend to myself that I wasn't a little freaked out so concentrate instead on wondering how visitors find their way around.

At the end of our shift, Davina leaves with me to walk to the car park. I ask if it's Jodie's day off because I haven't seen, or heard, her. Davina rolls her eyes and tells me to be careful of her. You can't trust Jodie apparently. I withhold judgement trying not to be swayed by the fact I'm not sure I like her, there's something aggressive about her. Her glares, out of tune singing and generally hostile demeanour probably. Not liking her, however, doesn't automatically mean she's not trustworthy. It simply means I don't like her.

Davina come to a sudden stop then asks me to wait she won't be long then disappears into the gift shop where she stands in a huddle with the woman who works in there. I want to leave now because the Manor is open and visitors are beginning to arrive but I don't want to be rude and walk away. I enter the shop to tell Davina, I need to go. The woman she's speaking to glares at me and purses her lips. I ignore her unfriendliness, smile brightly and introduce myself. She stares blankly but slightly belligerently at me. Great, I think while continuing to smile. My mouth aches with the falseness, then I begin to imagine myself looking more and more like a demented clown.

'Davina and I are having a private conversation,' she tells me coldly.

I don't say anything but I'm not sure if having a private conversation in a public place really works. I simply nod then leave. Thankfully, Davina follows me out.

Walking back to the car-park, Davina tells me the woman is Susie and she's having a 'difficult' time at the moment with Ivo and Caitlin, the two main managers. I don't bother to ask what she means by 'difficult'. After all, I don't know the woman, I'm not sure after my first contact with her. I even like her so frankly, not interested in whatever difficult time she may or may not be having at the moment. I focus instead on the rather lovely bag I spotted for sale in the shop. It was a tartan (naturally) but a lovely heathery purple and dull green. Davina rolls her eyes again. She's good at it only this time she adds a sigh.

Don't bother to buy it in there, she tells me because I can get it for nearly half the price at the gift shop in the castle down the road. The castle down the road? Really? There's a real, *bona-fide* castle *down the road*. I am lost in admiration for a few minutes at how someone can just say it like that. As if it's an everyday occurrence; a castle down the road. Of course, in Scotland it probably is but where I come from, there are no castles down any road except maybe a fake one or two built by someone who won the Lotto and is trying to be someone other than who they really are.

The Davina tells me the Dowager Duchess goes to the wholesalers at the end of the season and buys everything at a much-reduced price, puts it all in the Gift Shop at the start of the next season and quadruples the price.

I guess that's how the rich stay rich while the rest of us don't.

Wednesday 26th

Today I officially meet Ivo, the General Manager. It's not the first time I've seen him. My first encounter with him was on my first day when he came down to the Housekeepers' cupboard, looked me up and down, then told me in an I'm-just-letting-you-know-who's-in-charge voice, which is, sadly for him squeaky and not very authoritative, to bring the vacuum cleaner up to the back-door to suck up the wet leaves on the door mat.

Really? Not sure it's good to suck up wet leaves with a vacuum cleaner. Electricity and water? Not a good combination.

Anyway, he is hated, loathed and despised (no, that's not hyperbole, I'm probably underplaying the extent to which he is hated) by most of the staff except Jodie which isn't, I feel, much of a validation. Still, I can't work out why everyone makes such a fuss about him. He seems pleasant enough if a little narcissistic. You know the type I mean. He asks you a question about yourself but doesn't wait for the answer because he's actually not interested and wants to get back to talking about more important things – himself.

Then I get his whole CV with embellishments and sidebars in the fifteen minutes I have to stand in front of him. I say have because I can't get a word in edgewise and short of turning my back and walking away, I am forced to stand and listen because, sadly, he is my boss.

That's fifteen minutes of my life I'll never get back. I feel a bit cross at the end of it. And I'm pretty sure he'd have gone on for longer if some kind person from the outside world hadn't phoned for him. It is a call he has to take because it's important and he's important and anything to do with him is so important. It's only because I'm trapped in the narrow confines of the Housekeepers' cupboard where there isn't room to swing a cat, that I don't kick my heels in delight at his departure.

Note to self. Avoid any interaction with him that isn't absolutely necessary.

Thursday 27th

I arrive this morning to find it's Davina's day off so I am alone with Jodie. Not sure why but I feel uneasy around her.

'You have to watch that Davina,' she tells me in belligerent tones while hauling the vacuum cleaner out of the cupboard, 'she's a chameleon.'

'Really,' I reply, 'what do you mean?' I'm only being polite because I sense a gossip session is about to begin. I've worked out all the eye-rolling, teeth sucking and knowing-nods I see going on between most of the other staff are all a silent version of gossiping.

'You can't trust her. She'll say one thing to your face and something different behind your back.' Jodie explains staring at me while resting her chin on her hands which are folded on top of each other on the vacuum cleaner hose. I've taken to calling this 'the Housekeeper's Gossip Pose'.

'Hmmm,' I say backing away. I want to get on with my work. I hate rushing and there's only a limited amount of time to get it all done before the doors open and the visitors start flocking in. Call it inverted snobbery or whatever but some visitors think we're servants, I've heard one or two remarking on the 'maids', and it's a comment that doesn't sit well with my colonial sense of egalitarianism.

'So how many hours have you been given?' she asks. Her tone is pleasant enough but I can sense there's an edge to it. This, I suspect, is a loaded question. Will I give her the right answer? Since I don't know what that's likely to be, I go for honest instead.

'Six,' I say cautiously. I don't mention the option of getting more as the season progresses. Mainly because I'm not sure whether this will eventuate or not. It could be something to entice me in since I did point out in my interview, six hours a week on minimum wage won't even cover my petrol expenses. I am, however, not looking a gift horse in the mouth. A job is a job is a job.

'Yeah, same as me,' she replies so I guess I gave the right answer. She pushes past me, knocking my shins with the vacuum cleaner as she sweeps around the corner. She's a big woman so the force behind the sweeping is pretty impressive not to say painful. I almost wish I'd liked her before just so I can dislike now after that.

Later, I hear Jodie, Lucinda and Rory (the security guard/guide who always looks me up and down scathingly – can you look scathingly?) having a heated conversation about yoga. Never knew that was possible. Jodie does a couple of impressive toe touches just to show off how supple she is. It seems this is them all pretending they're having in a normal, innocuous conversation of the kind normal, ordinary people indulge in when suddenly, no longer able to contain themselves, they're off back to their favourite past-time moaning about the current chatelaine, the Dowager Duchess who resides in Cauldron Manor during the winter months when it is closed to public scrutiny. She's currently away on holiday. The first of many she apparently takes during the summer.

I try not to listen. I prefer to make up my own mind about people. I suspect those who do the employing of staff and wage-paying of said staff are often subjected to being gossiped and gossiped about.

I wonder if my staff ever talked about me like that. Probably. It goes with the territory. I feel a little sorry for the Dowager Duchess.

It does seem an odd thing to me, however, to open your house to let total strangers wander through nosing around your personal life. Not criticising, just pondering.

I get back to vacuuming because it doesn't look as if Jodie is about to do any more today.

Friday 28th

I finally manage to get a bit of dusting done today. This means I must be moving a bit faster with the vacuum cleaner. God, I hate that vacuum cleaner; it's heavy, cumbersome and so last century. For the first couple of days or so, my back and arms ached horribly. I try to think of it as exercise.

I get to do upstairs when Davina is working because downstairs is her territory but I have to go downstairs when Jodie's working because upstairs is her territory. This territorial thing is slightly unnerving. Jodie and Davina are actually territorial about the vacuum cleaners. Not lying. Davina has the pink one while Jodie, the red. Seriously. Vacuum cleaners.

Anyway, I don't think Jodie does dusting. I can write my name in the dust on most of the furniture and ornaments in the upstairs rooms. I test this out on a painting of a ghastly ancestor in the portrait gallery. In the corner, I use my finger to write my name and yep, I can see it where the black glossy paint catches the light. To be fair, I hate dusting in there too. All those gloomy men, and occasional woman, wearing their fancy dress, their eyes following my every move. I can almost hear them tutting at my perfunctory dusting. I dust my name off. I have no wish to anger the ancestors. They look pretty cruel and bloodthirsty to me.

In the main bedroom, which is open to the public, I also notice there's mouse poo on the four-poster silk, hand-embroidered bed-cover. As I'm not sure what to do about it or who I have to tell, I flick it onto the floor with the duster and suck it up with the vacuum cleaner. This place probably has more rats and mice scurrying around and poo-ing in the wainscoting than … well, than were in the sewers of Victorian London. I decide to ignore it for the moment.

I go back downstairs and am putting the vacuum cleaner away when Rory appears behind me, waving a blue dusting cloth.

'You left this on the floor upstairs,' he tells me. He sounds triumphant. Not sure why.

'okay,' I say. Then add 'thanks,' when I see he's waiting for more.

'That's okay,' he says smiling patronisingly, handing me the cloth.

Eeek!

MAY

Monday 1– Friday 5

For the whole of this week, Rory has managed, somehow, to find a cloth (or cloot as they call them) I've apparently left somewhere in one of the rooms. I'm getting seriously paranoid and am convinced he's putting them there. I'm sure the duster I take with me upstairs is always the same one I return downstairs with. He seems to take great delight in telling me about any other minor infraction I commit, which can be anything from: not hooking the door to the tower properly to the wall; missing vacuuming the carpet at the bottom of the upstairs sitting room stairs; not removing flower petals from the tables/windowsills; moving books out of alignment; moving chairs, photographs and ornaments into the path of the infra-red alarms.

I could go on but honestly, my mind can't deal with such an overload of pettiness. I did suggest it might be ghosts moving the ornaments which prompted him to roll his eyes and laugh heartedly. Lucinda on the other hand, embraced this explanation with all the enthusiasm of a member of Ghost Hunters International (a telly programme I used to enjoy but not any more. I feel it's a little too close to home and I'm unnerved by it now). See. See, she says to Rory jabbing the air in front of his nose with her long, thin fingers, I'm not the only one who thinks this place is haunted. Behind her back, Rory rolls his eyes at me. I think he's on the edge of liking me.

I tell him I have a mission for him should he choose to accept. I know he will pretend to resist but as he's as nosy as everyone else, he won't be able to. I tell him I've left a blue cloth hidden somewhere upstairs and he has until Friday to find it. If he does, I will bake him a cake. He grins and I know I've hooked him.

As we walk back to the car-park, Davina asks me where I've hidden the cloth. I'm not sure whether or not I should tell her I haven't hidden one anywhere. Which means, of course, Rory will never find it.

I notice at the end of the week, there's never a mention of the cloth and he no longer seems to find any I've apparently left or dropped. I wonder how long he looked for it. On the plus side, he now seems to like me and we enjoy a bit of jolly banter on the mornings he works, when he always greets me with 'Gidday cobber,' while I laugh obligingly at his accent, correct his pronunciation and don't bother to explain New Zealanders don't tend to say 'cobber'.

Small things...

Monday 8th

It's now 3 or so weeks since I started this job and I feel I am coming to grips with the difficult concept of vacuuming, dusting, dodging mouse poo and avoiding gossip. I have now met most of the summer staff including Alice, the kiosk coordinator and ticket seller who works in a little box outside the gates (not sure what the co-ordinator bit is about but if it makes her feel important, who am I to comment) and both the ticket collectors who sit inside the front door and work alternate days, Lucinda and Elspeth.

Lucinda may talk incessantly but Elspeth scares me. She knows everyone and everything within a 10 miles radius, (seriously everyone and to whom they are related or married or having an affair with and so on). She actually told me she knows my neighbours well. This is slightly scary for two reasons: one she actually knows where I live when I know I haven't told her and two, I don't even know my neighbours, never seen them, never met them, never spoken, so how do *they* even know they're my neighbours?

I've now met the other guide/security guard Colm who is an ex-Detective Inspector from Inverness, which unnerves me slightly. Not sure why but I think it has something to do with the way he looks at me as if I'm guilty of something. Maybe it's just his way. Maybe he's done it for so long, it's now just second nature to him. Maybe I'm a perpetually guilty person.

I also meet the cafe manager, Fenella (a vibrant, good-natured young woman who doesn't look old enough to be out of school) and 2 other seasonal housekeepers who seem to spend most of their two working hours moaning about what a god-awful job it is. Well, true it's certainly not my career of choice but I feel I have done worse. Pulling heads off prawns in a fish factory in Western Australia springs to mind. Truly, much, much worse.

One thing they all seem to have in common is a propensity for gossiping and moaning. It's clearly the glue binding them all together. I can't bear it, gossip is potentially dangerous and almost always poisonous but no matter how hard I try, I can't always avoid hearing it.

The constant complaining theme runs along the lines of: The Dowager Duchess is hard work, you have to mind your ps and qs, she'll pull you up on any little thing but she's also such a lovely person. Mind you, it's the 'she's such a lovely person' but that's usually the precursor to a full-on gossp-about-her session.

She's the second wife of the late Duke – who has a number of children from a previous marriage which was dissolved (is that a polite word for 'divorced'?) because of his excessive drug snorting, drinking and randiness. Those children include the current reigning Duke and several siblings. There's a few. I lose track. The Dowager, on the other hand, has only one son from a previous liaison who from all accounts is gormless and spoilt. He could be a simpleton. He does something in Nairobi although no one is sure what exactly but possibly involves a lot of drinking and getting into trouble but because no one actually knows for certain, I feel there's a lot of speculation going on. I'll wait until I meet him before passing judgement.

Apparently, there was huge outrage when it was revealed the late Duke, after popping his clogs, left the current Dowager the right to remain in Cauldron Manor during her lifetime and to do with it as she chooses. It's her job to run the business side of it because (I'm reading between the lines so could have it entirely wrong) it is the revenue from the Manor which keeps her in the style to which she is accustomed.

Cauldron Manor is still the present Duke's shack but he has to hang fire before making any claim or taking possession as long as his stepmother still breathes which, according to rumour didn't go down to well when it first came out, as it means she has absolute control over it during her lifetime. There's been, by all accounts, a few stand-offs by the portcullis where he's demanded entrance and she's refused. I spend a few happy minutes imagining her standing at one end of the drawbridge with a line of gardeners, rakes at the ready standing behind her while he stands on the other side with a line of gamekeepers and ghillies, shotguns and fishing tackle poised for action, standing behind him.

I kind of feel for him. Especially when she's calling the shots. I also suspect, reading between the lines, the outrage possibly could also have a lot to do with the fact she doesn't come from a posh family so she's a commoner. And she's also American. How did I miss that? Yep, as a colonial, I totally get how that must rankle. I mean who the hell knows what her antecedents might be? Heaven forbid they might be common ones.

Anyway, upon her death, the current Duke can then do what he likes with the Manor. In the meantime, it seems he's gone to court numerous times contesting the old Duke's Will and has, on more than one occasion, tried to get her evicted and so on but it turns out the old Duke's Last Will and Testament is watertight. Not sure what the fuss is about since the current Duke will get it eventually when The Dowager flops off her perch. Though true, if I were her, I wouldn't get too close to him or eat anything prepared by him because that's as good a motive for murder as any I've heard.

Tuesday 9th

Davina decides I am to work with her as the Dowager's other housekeeper during the winter after she moves back into the Manor. I'm choosing to go with the flow because a job is a job is a job. And it means Davina likes me. Apparently, the previous Head Housekeeper, Rochelle, just suddenly up and left without warning sometime the previous January after fewer than 6 months on the job, which left Davina in the lurch. She insists there is too much for one person to do. The summer housekeepers are laid off over the winter.

I speculate as to why Rochelle may have left but Davina seems a bit vague about it. I can't ask though because I'm sticking to my moral high ground about refusing to gossip.

The mouse poo is getting worse. I wonder if they're breeding and whether I should say something. I tentatively ask Davina if there's ever a mouse problem in the Manor.

'Oh aye,' she says, 'horsehair mattresses don't help.'

Horsehair mattresses! Really? I feel slightly sick.

'But no one sleeps on them?' I ask more in hope than anything else but it transpires the bed with the mouse poo is actually The Dowager's own bed, the one she sleeps on when she lives in the Manor during the winter. I try to imagine what it must be like to sleep in a mattress made from dead horses' hair in which mice like to make their home.

Nope, my mind refuses to go there.

Oh, maybe I should say something about the poo to someone then.

Wednesday 10th

One of the other summer housekeepers has left. I met her once. She stood at the bottom of the stairs leaning her chin on her hands resting on the vacuum cleaner hose (I must practise this but I don't seem to be the right height) while grumbling with Jodie who was doing the same chin resting thing while standing on the landing at the top of the stairs. They moan about the old staff because they are new staff and are pro the new management, Ivo and his offsider, Caitlin. According to them, because this is only Ivo and Caitlin's first season, all the old staff hate them because they've changed things, and the old staff hate the changes because they're 'old', 'boring', and 'stuck in their ways'. Everyone else, i.e. the old staff, seem to gripe about Ivo and Caitlin. They all to a man/woman, old and new, however, gossip about The Dowager.

Anyway, I'm now offered her hours and a couple of Cauldron Manor Holiday bothys to clean. From 6 hours a week to 10. Hell, at this rate I might get to be full-time before I die. I try not to look at my balance when I withdraw money from the card machine. As long as the damn thing still gives me money, I must be managing on my meagre income all right.

Thursday 11th

Today, amid great excitement, I'm told I am to meet the Dowager Duchess before she goes off on another holiday. She's already had one since I started working here. Must be nice. She doesn't live in Cauldron Manor during the summer months but takes herself off to a smallish house up the road while the Manor is open to the public. I get the impression The Dowager views this small house in the same light as a

New Zealander would about, say, a tent. Moving up the hill to this other house is the equivalent to a camping holiday for her so she keeps going off on holidays to rich friends' homes or to her flat in Paris because the hardship gets a bit much for her after a while.

I haven't seen this house as it's situated at the other end of the estate but Davina goes up to clean it when she's finished at the Manor. She usually goes up with someone called Calis who is the Manor's conservator because it turns out, it's also this Calis's job to do all the Dowager's laundry. I am surprised. Does the Dowager not know how to use a washing machine? It turns out, however, none of her personal clothing gets washed in a machine, Calis the Conservator washes it all by hand.

Even her smalls!

Blimey.

Anyway, Calis the Conservator is away on holiday and has been since I started.

'You'll like Calis the Conservator,' Davina keeps saying but because she keeps saying it, I begin to suspect I might not. She also tells me Calis the Conservator can seem pretty intimidating but really, it's all only a front. Front or not, intimidating is still intimidating. She always ends this statement with 'but you'll be able to handle her.'

This does not bode well.

It is Ivo's offsider, Caitlin who is also The Human Resources Manager and my immediate boss, who comes down to tell me about my 'diaried' meeting with the Dowager. I say 'comes down' because the Manor office is at the top of a tower up some narrow windy worn stone stairs. I'm not sure but I think it's dangerous. I tend to hold onto the rope handrail with both hands and grip very tightly. Still, my thighs get a good workout so it must be a good thing.

The Human Resources Manager is young enough to be my daughter. I call her sweetie and patronise her but I think she likes it because she's very young for the job and I'm too old to be told what to do by someone far less experienced than I in dealing with staff relations. She possibly knows this because she talks to me about the problem of Jodie.

We are supposed to work 2 hours a day from 8 until 10. Jodie clocks in at 8 but downs tools around 9, wanders around talking to anyone who will listen usually complaining about me because apparently, I took some hours off her, not sure how I managed that but clearly, I'm cleverer or just more devious than I realise, but then she clocks out at 10. Therefore, she works for an hour and gets paid for two.

Just pay her for one hour I say, that should put a stop to it. Or she'll leave. Either will do. Can't stand her myself, she's a bully and tries to intimidate by talking very loudly.

Caitlin then admits she meets Jodie for coffee and they've become sort of friends. Big mistake, I tell her. Be friendly but never friends because it makes situations like this when you have to discipline someone, pretty difficult.

I don't get to meet The Dowager after all. She is far too busy trying to get her clothes packed because she's off to France in the morning to her flat in Paris. She actually calls Calis the Conservator back off her holiday to pack her suitcase for her. Is this a Conservator's job? I suppose it depends on how old the suitcase and/or the clothes are. Or maybe how old the Dowager Duchess is.

Friday 12th

This morning Rory, the security guard/guide tells me he's overheard Jodie complaining to Affie...Effie...Offie, about me. I roll my eyes and tut. Do I really want to know what she said? No. Mainly because I can guess. She's not a person of great imagination. He tells me anyway because he loves to gossip. And he likes me and it's good to have someone on your side. He keeps telling me, he knows when I've done upstairs because it's clean. He's said it several times now, or possibly many times. I tend to just thank him because I suspect he wants to moan about Jodie and seriously, I don't like her enough to want to waste any headspace on her when I have other, more important and interesting things to think about. I know he's right though. Jodie just vacuums because it's impossible to get away with not doing that. The stones and dirt would be a give away but she can get away with not doing any dusting.

Anyway, according to Rory, Jodie claims I'm a greedy cow. Well, I don't like Jodie so I'm not really bothered but I act suitably horrified and am a little bit gratified to see how pissed off Rory is on my behalf. Clearly, he's forgiven me for hiding a cloth too well for him to find. I wonder if I should admit there was never any cloth. Hmm maybe not. I half suspect he likes me because he thinks I'm as clever as he is (never cleverer of course. That wouldn't do).

Later, I hear him talk to Lucinda downstairs about it. Then they go off into a gripe session about Jodie. Turns out she worked here last year too and no one could stand her then. It seems to me no one can stand anyone in this place. Does anyone like anyone, I find myself wondering?

Monday 15th

I meet Calis the Conservator today. Not an experience I ever wish to repeat.

I don't realise she's standing behind watching me vacuum so I get a bit of a shock when I turn to see her standing in the doorway. She gives me an odd smile (not entirely sure it is a smile but I'll give her the benefit of the doubt) which enhances an illusion of a sprite-like creature shuffling towards me. For a minute I freak out wondering if this is some weird spectre doing a spot of haunting. To my relief, she speaks although the relief is short-lived.

You're a New Zealander?' is the first thing she says to me, making it sound like a disease. Her lip curling is subtle. I don't get a chance to answer before she launches into: 'My husband and I went for a holiday down your way. He worked there years ago and enjoyed it.' Then she looks me straight in the eye and adds, 'God knows why. What a boring country it is.'

For a minute I'm completely floored which I realise, in the next minute, is her intention.

Oh, nice. Not sure what to say. I just smile and say, 'what a shame.' Davina says she's intimidating but I think she meant nasty.

Then later she calls me up to one of the bedrooms and tells me I'm not vacuuming the silk carpet properly. She's on her knees stroking it lovingly.

Yep, weird.

'Only with the pile, not against it. And try to keep the nozzle in the air just above it. Don't touch the carpet. If Mrs Upstairs (that's what I call the Dowager in my head but not what Calis calls her; she uses the proper nomenclature) sees that, she'll go mad.' She explains. Quite nicely actually. It is a bit disarming. I wonder if this is her intention. I decide to reserve judgement until I know her better. I am so taken aback by her sudden change in disposition, however, I miss the instruction about where to hold the nozzle. It's only later when I think about it, I realise what a stupid thing she's told me to do. Hold it above the carpet! Really? So, I am to vacuum the air above the carpet. Not sure my arm muscles are up to it apart from the sheer pointlessness of it. The carpet is dirty, not the air above it.

Oh, this is going to be fun.

Not.

Wednesday 17th

This morning Jodie catches me in the housekeepers' cupboard. I'm usually early enough to avoid her since she refuses to start even a couple of seconds before she's rostered on. A couple of minutes makes no difference to me except it allows me to dodge her.

She's aggrieved apparently for two reasons. First, one of the vacuum cleaners has stopped working which means she has to get one from the shop, which is downstairs, a long way downstairs. Pretty much through a dungeon. I don't see the problem since she spends most of her time down there anyway, gossiping and moaning to the Shop Liaison Staff – (yep, one of those made up designations to make shop assistants feel they are more than just shop assistants, though personally, being a shop assistant would be just fine for me) one of whom is Affie...Effie...Offie who I met on my first morning and she seems to have a love/hate relationship with Jodie - but second, and I suspect this is the real reason for her aggrievement (not sure if that's a word but it will do) is because I've been given extra hours and a couple of the holiday bothys on the Estate to clean. These were the jobs of the other housekeeper who just quit.

'Well you're welcome to the holiday bothys,' I tell her. I'm not entirely happy about cleaning them as I have to do them on Sunday morning because that's the changeover day but it means I have a 6-day week and cleaning is hard work.

'I can't work Sundays. I've told them this. I have four small children.' She says, well shouts actually. And she's gone red in the face.

'Well okay, have my other day,' I say trying to slide along the wall to get away from her.

'I can't work that day either! I've told them what hours I can work and none of those fit,' she declares heatedly while pulling the vacuum cleaner out from the cupboard in such a manner it makes me suspect she's the one responsible for the other cleaner breaking but it also means I will have to go down through the dungeon to get the shop one. I'm annoyed to see even though she is doing upstairs, she's taking the downstairs cleaner.

Oh, see how petty I am becoming.

'okay, so if you can't do any of the days these jobs have to be done on then what's your problem?' I don't roll my eyes. I want to but I'm a bit scared of her. You know how it is with people who are always aggrieved. They're aggrieved because they want to be but they also always think they're right and justified to feel aggrieved. It's a no-win situation as far as I'm concerned.

'That's not the point,' she fairly spits at me, 'but I would have liked to have been asked. I wasn't even asked.' I duck to avoid the spray.

Oh, here we go, narcissists rule. Thank god, I'm not inside her head. What a tortuous spaghetti-like mishmash of aggrievement it must be in there. I'm also annoyed she's put me in this impossible position over something so minor. We are talking about another 4 hours. Really. Truly. 4 hours.

Maybe being an employee isn't so great after all.

'And I've never met the Dowager. And I've worked here for 2 seasons!'

Oh, I can see she is really getting into this now. I think it's the way her voice rises and becomes very shrill. And the way she positions herself in front of the door so I can't get out except by turning around and heading down to the other one but as she has the vacuum cleaner positioned in front of my legs, I am not about to jump over it and make a run for it. I have my pride.

'Well, neither have I,' I counter.

I wish I had to courage to kick the bitch. Really, she has her face right up against mine. I'm not sure my being given a few extra hours and her not being asked about it really justifies this kind of aggression.

'Yes, but you're going to,' she adds bitterly before turning and pulling the vacuum cleaner out the door behind her banging various bits of ancient furniture as she goes. It is precisely for this reason we are instructed to carry it and not pull it behind us even though it has little wheels for this purpose. I tend to ignore this injunction and pull it because the damn thing is so heavy and cumbersome but I'm always careful not to knock the furniture or run the lead around corners which marks the door jambs. Doesn't seem to bother her though. I think I'll ask Davina to swap days off which means I'll only have one day working with her, Jodie the Joyless.

Thursday 18th

Calis the Conservator comes up to me as I vacuum the carpet in The Dowager's bedroom and repeats her instructions about how to do it properly. I am already doing it the right way, my arm muscles are trembling with the effort of vacuuming air, but I'm sensing there's a lot of ego in this place. I bite my tongue. If it makes her feel better to talk to me as if I'm stupid, let her get on with it. Then suddenly she says 'she likes me and wants me to stay over the winter.'

What the hell? I've barely exchanged a word with the woman. I hear little alarm bells going off. Beware the people who suck up to you immediately. There's usually another agenda going on. Then she tells me to be careful of Jodie. I feel I am being cautioned on whose 'side' I must be.

'She spends too much time talking and sucking up to Caitlin and Ivo.'

I'm guessing from the malicious way she says it, this not a good thing. Working my way through the internal politics in this place is exhausting. And Calis the Conservator is part of the old regime after all.

She then tells me she's worked for Mrs Upstairs since she was 18.

18! She must be at least 60 now. At least. She could even be older because the soft Scottish sun seems to preserve skin instead of turning it into old leather like the sun in New Zealand does. I am shocked. My mind boggles at the thought. At 18, the only thing I was interested in was spending my days hanging out at beach parties getting stoned with my friends. And the days I didn't spend hanging out at beach parties, I was in bed recovering from all the hanging out at beach parties. My employment was a constantly revolving door of different jobs and duration depending on my boredom threshold which was, at 18 if I recall, pretty low though as I was stoned for most of the time, it is difficult to remember accurately.

So, if she is around 60, that's a good 40 plus years working in the same place. I'm so astonished, I have to sit down. Then I realise this is also about her letting me know her higher-up-than-me place in the pecking order.

Do I care?

Nope.

Then I remember to tell her about the mouse poo on the Dowager Duchess's bed which even Jodie has noticed and begun moaning about.

I see a dramatic side to her then. Calis I mean, not Jodie. I didn't expect such an extreme reaction. She acts as if she thinks I am deliberately enticing mice inside to poo all over the silk bed covers and carpets. Luckily, I can escape to finish the vacuuming. I later see her dragging Ivo upstairs. I wonder if now it's his fault. I'm sure Calis the Conservator will make him feel it is.

I meet one of the gardeners on the way out. He likes to chat to me about New Zealand. He went there on holiday once and loved it. This experience has helped us form a bond. I still can't come to terms with Calis the Conservator having the same job for 40 odd years so I ask how long he's worked at the Manor. 20 years he tells me. I am suddenly struck by how different this world is. I mention how Calis the Conservator has worked for Mrs Upstairs since she was 18. He likes my calling the Dowager Duchess, Mrs Upstairs and chortles for a minute or two. Oh her, he says at my mention of Calis. He doesn't like her. I can tell by the way his lip curls. He then tells me she hasn't always worked at the Manor. For a while, she went off to work at the castle down the way. They threw a really big leaving party for her apparently after Mrs Upstairs enticed her back to the Manor. They must have really liked her, I say trying not to look as bemused by the thought as I actually feel. Perhaps I've underestimated her, perhaps I'm not such a good judge of character, perhaps... perhaps.

He laughs and walks away. Oh aye, he says over his shoulder, they threw that party after she'd left.

Friday 19th

I now have a key to Cauldron Manor. True it's only to the back door by what were once the servants' quarters, the old butler's pantry to be precise, but you have to start your social climbing somewhere. It's because I work on the weekends and Davina, who has a key, doesn't. Last weekend I had to call her in to unlock the door for us. I think it is far-sighted of me to request a key and so avoid this happening again.

Ivo made a great fuss about giving it to me. I half expected him to request police clearance or something. Considering the whole place is alarmed to the turrets, I can't imagine what he feared I might get up to now I've got access and it's not as if I have the alarm code so the access is pretty limited. Then I realised he expected me to be grateful because he thought he was bestowing some great honour on me by giving me possession of this key which I would also be taking home with me.

I wasn't to give it to anyone else. Or even let anyone know I had this key. I had to sign a book saying this. As if I know anyone who'd give a toss.

Ivo the Idiot.

Sunday 21st

I meet Jodie at the back door this morning. She's aghast to see I have a key.

'Oh, aren't you the privileged one,' she sneers. I resist the urge to ram it up her nose.

'Just being organised,' I reply much more calmly than I am feeling. 'After all, there's no one to let us in on the weekend,' I add. I try not to sound smug but not entirely sure I succeed.

She glares at me before stomping down to the Housekeepers' Hideout.

As I reluctantly follow her down, I'm hoping she will be so pissed off at me, she'll simply get the vacuum cleaner and disappear upstairs ASAP.

No such luck.

I'm halfway down the ramp when she shouts out to me that she's threatened to quit unless management buys a new vacuum cleaner. Seems a bit of an over-reaction to me but I play dumb. I raise my eyebrows and look suitably impressed which seems to satisfy her. She drags the other vacuum cleaner (the one from the shop downstairs) off upstairs banging it as she goes. I wonder how much longer this one will last.

If I think I've escaped her, I'm sadly mistaken. She hovers on the upstairs landing waiting for me to walk past below.

'I don't blame you,' she announces loudly which is a bit of a relief though I'm not sure what I'm not being blamed for. I try to wheel my vacuum cleaner past the bottom of the staircase and out of sight as quickly as I can. The goddesses are against me. The hose falls out. I expect it's because of all the chin leaning that gets done on it.

'I've never worked anywhere where so much gossiping goes on,' she continues from the landing.

Oh, yeah right and most of it would be by you, I think while trying to reattach the hose.

'And most of it comes from you middle-aged woman,' she adds spitefully.

Oh ouch.

I resist pointing out most of the gossip seems to be done by everyone irrespective of age. And I wonder how old you have to be before you qualify for being middle-aged. I'm pretty sure I'm not quite there yet.

Just then Calis the Conservator (what the hell is she doing here on a Sunday? Davina told me her usual days are Mondays and Thursdays. Then she did qualify the statement with: or any other day she fancies) walks past and loudly orders us to stop talking and get on with our work. Never thought I'd be pleased to see her.

'Who the fuck do you think you are ordering me about? I'll start work when I'm good and ready,' Jodie shouts at her really, really loudly and very, very angrily as she turns to stomp off upstairs.

'Did you hear that...' Calis the Conservator starts fairly spluttering with indignation which is interesting to watch but I decide I can't hang around to enjoy the spectacle and scuttle off to the Long Drawing Room. No way am I getting involved in their spat. I don't trust either of them not to turn it around on me.

At the end of her shift (I say hers because she still finishes an hour before I do), Jodie puts the shop vacuum cleaner in the cupboard. I had just met Affie...Effie...Offie from the shop downstairs who asks me where their cleaner is. I tell her we have borrowed it and will return it as soon as we've finished with it. Jodie, however, tells me in no uncertain terms I am not to return it but I am to leave it in our cupboard. I'm not game to take her on. I know how to pick my battles and it's impossible to get anywhere with someone who's always aggrieved and who always thinks they're right.

'If they want it, they can come to get it,' she says glaring at me. I feel she is daring me to take it. She's making a point apparently. Not quite sure what the point is.

That she's a nutty, narcissistic gossip perhaps?

I wait for her to go off to wherever it is she goes while trying to fill in an hour (seems like a waste of energy. Surely it would be just as easy to actually do her work) before I return the cleaner to Affie...Effie...Offie. I do it quickly just in case Jodie decides to wander back and say, actually finish her day's work. The chances of that happening are pretty slim but you never know. I don't say anything because Affie...Effie...Offie and Jodie are as thick as thieves and Affie...Effie...Offie is one of Ivo's team who he brought in along with Caitlin and Fenella, the café manager, when he took on the CEO job.

A little bit of nepotism goes a long way.

Tuesday 23rd

We still don't have a new vacuum cleaner. Odd how this doesn't bother either Davina or me but apparently Jodie has refused to come into work until a new one is bought. Davina and I are very jaunty. It feels as if we're on holiday and the atmosphere has definitely lifted. Then I hear Davina and Calis the Conservator moaning about Jodie.

Calis the Conservator comes to find me and tells me to give the 2 guest bedrooms and The Dowager's bedroom a really good clean because it's not been done properly and she doesn't trust Jodie. I think that's a non-sequitur but I'm not about to say anything. I'm also not sure how much authority she has over me but I'm all for an easy life and going with the flow. Besides all this gossiping thing is really unnerving me. I can't remember working anywhere this bad for it. I'm also guessing the Monday-Thursday thing for Calis is pretty fluid since by my reckoning today is a Tuesday unless I've slept really heavily through a couple of days.

Wednesday 24th

I meet Miserable Murdo the Handyman today. He's about 60ish going on grumpy. I've seen him mooching around so know who he is by reputation but Davina actually introduces us this morning. He looks me up and down but then seems both disappointed and slightly puzzled. Maybe it's my bright purple, hand embroidered, hand beaded Indian tunic. Maybe it's the Berber headscarf I'm wearing today, the one I bought in Morocco last year. Maybe it's the fact I'm not dressed in the uniform of hoodie and skinny jeans. Maybe he's short-sighted and I don't look so young close up. But then, maybe it's just his usual expression. Either way, he barely greets me before he sits down behind the front desk and starts complaining about Ivo, Caitlin and, of course, Dowager Duchess.

Not sure I can deal with this surfeit of negativity and misery.

Thursday 25th

Jodie does come to work today but spends her two hours up in the office talking (complaining) to Caitlin. It's Davina's day off so I have to vacuum both upstairs and down. Well, when I say 'have to' I really mean I feel obliged because it is clear Jodie isn't going to and Lucinda is fretting about opening up and letting the public in to be confronted by a dirty carpet. Horror of horrors, think of the TripAdvisor reviews.

Calis the Conservator comes along and tells Lucinda, 'she'll go mad if she sees this.' I'm assuming she means the Dowager Duchess (or Mrs Upstairs as I continue to call her in a spirit of colonial rebellion) and she's not referring to... say, the Queen. I'm half tempted to not vacuum the carpet just to see if Mrs Upstairs really does go mad. Now that could be an interesting spectacle.

Unfortunately, my Catholic guilt and finely-honed sense of obligation kick in so I do it at a run. I then spend ½ an hour talking to Cassie in accounts who is an interesting middle-aged neatly dressed Spiritual Medium who gives me a lengthy but interesting description of all the spirits wafting around the Manor. I kind of believe her because I've caught sight of a few odd things out of the corner of my eye. There is a woman in a blue dress and white lace cap who has been seen many times by visitors and by staff. I think I've seen her without realising it. She floats mournfully around the Long Drawing Room. The fingerless daughter is another one apparently but she sticks to the rooms upstairs, the ones not open to the public. I feel a sense of relief. Not sure I could cope with running into her. At least the blue dress/white laced capped woman is a ghost with a bit of dignity who doesn't seem to feel the need to scare the hell out of anyone. Many have seen her but no one seems upset by the experience.

I wonder if she's the ghost who moves those ornaments which set the alarms off every morning and when I say every morning, I mean every… single… morning. The alarms are horrible and ear splitting which I guess is the point but we waste time trying to find which ornament is out of alignment. The alarm won't go off until whichever ornament or object it is, is moved out of the beam's way. It's never the same one.

Interesting.

Anyway, I clock out three-quarters of an hour late and text Caitlin to tell her what I've done and I expect to be paid for it. I don't mention Jodie's absence but since she was up in the office from 8-10, I assume Caitlin will understand.

Friday 26th

Jodie has walked out. Yee ha. She told Lucinda, the ticket collector she is going to 'show them'. Not sure what that means but I think she thinks she's leaving management, and by extension, the rest of us, in the lurch and they'll beg her to reconsider. Sadly for her but luckily for me and Davina, one of the café staff is looking for some extra hours so she's picked up some of Jodie's and I am to do the others. Davina and I forego the dusting after we've raced through the vacuuming so we can sit down and have a really good backstabbing session about Jodie.

Oh dear, see how they've turned me.

Monday 29th

Today I learn from Davina there is a clear distinction between summer staff who work for the Estate, which runs the business side of the Manor and the permanent staff who work all year and are paid some by Mrs Upstairs and some by the current Duke depending on whether they are indoor or outdoor staff. Most of which, particularly the outdoor staff like the gardeners and gamekeepers, is comprised of the descendants of old retainers who worked the Estate when Adam was a boy.

Davina's father was a gamekeeper as was his father and his father and so on. Davina's brother is the security guard who hangs out in the Manor when Mrs Upstairs is away (in case anyone decides to break in and make off with her vast collection of tacky bric-a-brac). Calis the Conservator has worked for the Dowager since 1979 as has Murdo the Handyman. Mrs Upstairs' private chef Manfred has worked for her since 1975. Not sure if this a good thing or not. I fear it makes them very insular. And grumpy. Calis the Conservator and Miserable Murdo the Handyman seem to walk around shrouded in a fine mist of negativity. I do my best to avoid it. And them.

The gardeners, some of whom I encountered on my first day and with whom I now enjoy a jolly good banter (this means they pokaye fun at my accent and I laugh obligingly) are also part of the Manor permanent staff and work throughout the winter. They all live in houses on the estate. I get the impression most of them were born in them. As were their fathers, and their fathers and so on. Not mothers though. Interesting. Now, this is a world I am not familiar with. I begin to wonder if I've slipped into a time warp and been shipped back to the 19th century.

JUNE

Sunday 4th

I go up to clean my first holiday cottage today. I say 'up' because it's a fishing bothy on the moor which is up unlike the forests or woods which are down. Miserable Murdo the handyman drives me up to it because I doubt my car will make it. It's nearly as old as I am and I don't want to wear it out. I only ever see Miserable Murdo looming around complaining, moaning and looking gloomy with Calis the Conservator in tow. He's always hanging out on the stairs by the ticket collector's table grousing about how miserable his life is. God, what is it with these people? He is a gangly morose man who speaks in a foreign tongue.

He tells me some long and complicated story about the late Duke and his many mistresses but I miss about 80% of it due to his foreign language problem (so he could have been talking about almost anything really). I ask him what language he speaks. He frowns, glowers at me and says English in a very terse tone and looks strangely at me but I think he is lying.

'What language do you speak?' he asks. He is being rude. I can tell from his tone. 'New Zealandish,' I say which shuts him up.

Monday 5th

I hear Calis the Conservator, Elspeth and Davina moaning about Ivo and how useless he is. I'm busy dusting ancient things on the landing and wonder if I'm the only one who takes my job seriously. Then I wonder why I do and why it annoys me when others don't. It is only dusting and a minimum waged job after all.

Ivo, it seems is both a liar and a buck-passer supremo. He never has your back according to Elspeth and will drop you in it as fast as he can to save himself. He's 'as slippery as an eel' and 'as selfish as a fox'. I sense their similes are a little dated and lack imagination.

He's management, I want to say, it's in their blood. That's why he's management and you're not.

'As for that bloody little cow Caitlin,' Calis the Conservator says, 'I trust her as far as I can throw her. Neither of them has any idea what they are doing and they strut around like they own the place. Can't stand the little cow myself.'

Yep. Nasty.

It's always easy to criticise but having been in the boss position myself, I know how wearying it is trying to keep everyone happy when all they actually want is to be is unhappy, complain about it and blame you. True my heart hasn't warmed to Ivo. I agree he's a first-class ego stroker (oh look at me, look at me!) but I'm not prepared to get up his nose. What's wrong with keeping your nasty opinions to yourself and just smiling sweetly? He doesn't have to know how I feel about him.

They go into a huddle then and start to talk about all the times they've caught him out lying. I'm pleased to see Davina breaks away from them and comes upstairs to find me. When she sees I'm on the landing within earshot, she rolls her eyes and nods her head in the direction of Elspeth and Calis the Conservator who seem to be hissing like a couple of snakes.

I tell her I don't like gossip. I've said this right from the start and she actually appears to be taking it on.

She does let slip Rochelle the previous Head Housekeeper who walked out, probably did so because of gossip and Calis the Conservator.

I'm getting the picture.

Wednesday 7th

The Dowager Duchess has returned. Odd how the atmosphere has changed because even though she doesn't live in the Manor during the summer, she does nevertheless have a sitting room/office opposite the entrance where she hangs out, putting the wind-up everyone and shouting at visitors who dare to peer in through the window at her. Hasn't she heard of nets?

As a result of her potential presence, the gossiping is less intense but everyone looks a little strained. I haven't met the woman yet but am now feeling a little reluctant to do so. I'm wary of the effect her proximity has one everyone. What does that say about her actual presence?

Thursday 8th

Apparently, it's now part of my job to clean Mrs Upstairs' sitting room/office. Nightmare. She has more clutter than... well, I don't know anyone with more clutter. I'm not allowed to touch or move anything which makes cleaning a trifle difficult.

I don't think she's noticed it's summer and the fire is never lit so I'm not sure if I'm meant to retrieve all those bits of screwed up paper she tosses in there. I'm tempted to light a match and throw it in just to see what happens.

I am to make sure her kettle is always filled with filtered water even though the jug of filtered water actually sits on the tray right beside the kettle. Really? Not sure it's much of an art to filling a kettle nor, I would I have thought, is it complicated to lift a jug and pour its contents in but that's the aristocracy for you. Pretty damned domestically challenged apparently.

I also must remember to check her Harrods tea tin is full of her organic tea and make sure her glass teapot is clean. If it's got any brown scum ie tannin from the tea, I am to pour in some vinegar and brown rice (not sure why it has to be brown but maybe it's healthier for the vinegar), give it a swish around and rinse out thoroughly. To my surprise, it works. The glass is shiny and scum free. The teapot looks new. Must remember this.

Davina also told me if the filtered water jug is empty, rather than walking back through the Manor to get more from a special filtered water tap in the kitchen I am to just fill it up from the hand-basin in the toilet. I also wash her cup and water glass in the basin too. Can't imagine it's going to kill her. And the water in this isolated part of the country tastes all right to me. I wonder if she can tell the difference.

There are so many photos around her office it almost amounts to sensory overload. And they are all, except for a couple, of her. She's fairly tall, rather large and round with big teeth and hair. All the photos are posed with lots of soft light, dreamy, filmy backgrounds and she's positioned in such a way as to try to make her look slim and lithe. You know the ones I mean. They try to make the subject look ethereal and beautiful. Not happening. She looks as if she's just eaten something sour. I wonder what she really looks like.

Those that are not of her, are of her son instead. Quite a large painting of him hangs above the mantelpiece over the fireplace. He's good looking in that *I've-never-really-had-to-do-any-work-but-just-lounge-around-languidly* poppy eyed, full-lipped way.

She also has a number of books on the subject of, oh yes, the aristocracy. I expect it comes from being a commoner. And American. She's got to bone up on all the do's and don'ts otherwise she's in danger of giving herself away. From my limited experience, the British aristocracy is always quick to pick up on imposters. I expect, however, having pots of money, a grand title and a Manor helps.

Friday 9th

I have now fully embraced my new late onset career as a domestic servant and it is coming along a treat. I have mastered the technique of careful dusting, that is to say, managing not to break anything and or move any little knick-knack into the path of the infrared security beam. As there are possibly hundreds of ornaments, photos, and books, if I do move one out of kilter, it takes ages and lots of swearing to find which one it is. This is not the one the ghost moves. This is after we've, i.e. me, have found that one, pushed it back into place, turned the alarms off, dusted then turned the alarms back on. There's always something catching the edge of the beam and then nobody likes me while we all search frantically for it as the alarms are destroying our ear drums.

As for the specialised vacuuming, yes well actually it is specialised. I hover the Hoover over Mrs Upstairs' handwoven, ancient, silk, drawing room carpet watched by Calis the Conservator's eagle eyes, making sure the sucky bit doesn't actually come in direct contact with say ancient carpet, by vacuuming the air above it with careful strokes IN THE DIRECTION OF THE PILE. This is important. The muscles in my arms are becoming very defined so there's always an upside if you look for it.

Today, I ask The Conservator how the mouse poo is and she glares at me. I wonder if she does, in fact, think I may have something to do with it. I suspect the mouse problem is now bit out of control because I've noticed the number of mouse traps placed around the room are now so numerous, it's impossible for me to vacuum without setting a few off. Mind you, I'm probably not always as careful as I should be. But Miserable Murdo seems to be full of admiration for these clever mice who can set the traps off without being caught in them. I don't want to disillusion him.

Wednesday 14th

Yesterday, while doing my specialised dusting (and believe me there are shed loads of ornaments, objet d'art, books and furniture to dust), I came across a beautiful, ornately carved little box in Mrs Upstairs' Drawing Room.

I use her name with reverence as do the rest of the staff even when they're moaning about her and even though she's originally a commoner who married into the peerage but really 'hasn't she done well for herself'. Well, I guess if you put nabbing yourself a titled husband who leaves you his Manor after he flops off his perch on a par with say completing a PhD in Astrophysics, then yes, I guess she has done well for herself.

As I am curious by nature, I carefully lift the lid, expecting to find something exquisite, something worthy of being kept so carefully and in a box so publicly displayed, but what do I find? A Bounty bar! Really! How disappointing. Though I'm relieved it is a Bounty rather than say, a Mars bar. She would have definitely gone down in my estimation then. Not that she's high in it anyway. I'm getting sick of being told I am to meet her today but after hanging around for far longer than I want to, I am then told she is too busy to see me and it will have to be another time. Of course, she is a Dowager Duchess and I am merely a housekeeper but it's still rude.

Thursday 15th

Today Calis the Conservator takes me on a tour around the parts of the Manor not open to the public. I think she and Davina have decided I'm going to stay on to work over the winter. Not entirely sure how I feel about it. I'm not hugely fond of housework but I guess, I am being paid to do it. Hey, I'm happy to go with the flow.

She starts off by taking me into her lair, which Davina had already shown me but I don't want to ruin it for Calis so I try to act suitably impressed which seems to gratify her. I don't let on I am actually only impressed by the fact someone is able to work in an environment so medieval, I'm surprised movie moguls aren't down there negotiating to use it as part of a set for a medieval murder mystery. Cadfael sets are luxurious by comparison.

Calis tells me when she first worked at the Manor before it was opened to the public and run solely as a private house, she wasn't allowed to leave the room at all. The laundry had to be brought to her for washing, ironing, and mending. That was in the 1980s. I'm sure she says the 1980s and not 1880s. I could be wrong. It's possible she is that old. All that steam in there may have kept her skin moist and youthful.

She then unlocks a cupboard which turns out to be a linen graveyard. Shelves and shelves full of linen wrapped in tissue paper with little labels saying 'beyond repair'.

'Why keep it if it can't be used?' I ask, but she doesn't seem to have an answer except to say; 'she'll go mad if I tried to get rid of any.' I'm rapidly coming to the conclusion Mrs Upstairs has a very angry side to her. Either that or Calis the Conservator thinks she has.

'Would she notice?' I ask in all innocence. I say in all innocence because the look Calis gives me suggests she's heard a completely different question though when I run the question back in my mind, I not sure how it can be heard as anything different. Not sure why but the nanosecond of bonhomie she's shown me disappears really fast.

As she leads me up narrow stone stairs and along dark and creepy corridors, she's keen to tell me all about the late Duke's Will and the rift it's caused in the family. I say I'm sure he had his reasons and families are families. Who knows what goes on inside them? Mostly even the families don't know. Something tells me it's not safe gossiping with Calis the Conservator especially when she starts hinting about Mrs Upstairs' subsequent 'friends' and 'the ceilings she's seen' after the late Duke's death. It takes me a few minutes to work out what she means and when I do, I feel … well, not sure what but uncomfortable and slightly uneasy go only some way to explaining it. There's something disturbingly salacious about the way she's talking about the Dowager.

I tend to trust my gut feelings these days but it's clear she's put out by my not joining in with her. I can understand. It's no fun gossiping by yourself. I notice she cuts the tour short a bit quick and stomps off back to the laundry room without saying goodbye to me. Well, so much for that. I'm pretty sure I'll never find my way around upstairs ever again. Not bothered but I do feel I want to go home to have a shower.

Monday 19th

Today I advance further in my career as a domestic servant. I am promoted to doing some emergency cleaning in her summer residence.

She is away.

Again.

It's only when she's away the real cleaning can be done apparently because while she likes a clean house, she doesn't like watching it or being aware of it being cleaned. I have the same problem except I just don't like doing the actual cleaning; I wouldn't mind watching someone else do it, however.

Anyway, I go up with Calis the Conservator to polish floorboards in the dining room. It's the first time I've actually seen it and I must say, compared to the Manor, it is tiny; a mere 7 bedrooms and a teensy-weensy kitchen the size of my house but I suppose if you're used to living somewhere like Cauldron Manor then this must feel like camping in a small tent.

And the floorboard polishing? It's not just any old polishing. Oh no. On my hands and knees sweeties, on my hands and knees! I cover the boards with a special thick gluggy wax but thinly, very, very thinly. A thin layer is important because once it has dried, I have to rub it off... I mean polish... and if the layer is too thick it takes hours of rubbing to buff it up to a nice shine. I have, during this process, discovered some muscles across the top of my shoulders that until today I never knew existed. But they have been thoroughly exercised so that's a plus.

Calis is nice and chatty (though I use the word 'nice' carefully. Something about the combination of Calis the Conservator and the word 'nice' don't seem to go to well together) but she wants to gossip about Davina which makes me feel uncomfortable since Davina and I work together a lot and have built up a nice little 'I watch your back while you watch mine' rapport. She also gets a bit nastyy about Miserable Murdo the handyman (likes younger woman and his second wife was much, much younger) and Manfred, Mrs Upstairs' personal chef who has a chronic drink problem apparently and if Mrs Upstairs knew he still drank, she'll go mad. According to Calis the Conservator that is. To my dismay, I find I'm actually now beginning to feel quite eager to witness this 'going mad' thing the Dowager seems to have a propensity for. Unfortunately, I am beginning to suspect this is a stick the Calis the Conservator likes to beat us with.

Anyway, she seems to take a great delight in showing me where Manfred stashes his cans of lager around the kitchen. It makes me feel a bit uncomfortable. Like looking in someone's bedroom drawers). I have yet to meet Manfred but it transpires they are all really good friends and have been for years.

I discover Calis the Conservator's husband is also part of the gang. He worked for the Estate when he was younger. That's where they met but Calis the

Conservator went off and married someone else who ended up being an alcoholic so she left him. I guess this was when she ended up working at the Castle down the road where they threw a leaving party for her after she'd left.

I make no comment nor pass judgement.

Then Mrs Upstairs begged her (she repeats this several times so I'm beginning to doubt the veracity of it a little) her to come back to work for her so she did. She met up again with her soon to be the second husband and married him not long afterwards. Now they are all a jolly band of four though this was interrupted for a while by Miserable Murdo's much, much younger wife who didn't like them. According to Calis the Conservator that is. She thinks the wife probably felt threatened by them because they all go 'way back together'. Hmmm not sure how I feel about that. I do feel sure I don't want to be her enemy. Her husband, I decide must have a thick skin or he does as he's told. I sense you don't argue with her.

I tell her as little as possible about myself.

Monday 26th

After more than 3 months as a housekeeper, I feel at home in the Manor where because there are so many CCTV cameras everywhere, I feel I'm in a Manor House version of Big Brother. Just who will be watching me later? It's lucky in some respects I was brought up a Catholic because I am familiar and comfortable with the concept of someone much more important than me watching my every move. I make sure I comport myself with dignity and decorum.

I can now vacuum the space above priceless silk carpets with an air of accomplishment as if this is something I am born to, and polish floorboards on my hands and knees with all the grace of a yoga devotee.

I find, however, I am not becoming complacent but perhaps a little ho-hum about it. After all, as far as variety goes, there's not a lot of it about. Then today I am approached by the Estate Manager and someone who turns out to be a Head Gamekeeper.

Yes, a real live Gamekeeper.

He asks if I will consider taking on another task.

'Oh yes,' I say trying not to sound as if I was leaping at the opportunity for a bit of variety. 'What is it?'

'Beating,' says the gnarly gamekeeper. Apparently, there is much more to this Manor than just being a Manor. The Estate is so enormous; you'd think the Duke would be pleased someone like Mrs Upstairs has the responsibility of running the Manor thereby taking that particular burden off his shoulders.

So, the Estate is run by the Duke who speaks as little as possible to the Dowager (according to gossip) but as both Estate and Manor are intertwined, they have to work together. Still, if I were her, I'd definitely make my own cup of tea when he is around.

Anyway, after that little description – beating - my mind is immediately filled with ideas of aristocratic sadomasochistic, fetishistic practices, possibly in the form of wild parties. I try to contain my excitement.

'Beating! Beating what!' I ask guilelessly. It's not good to look too keen.

'Grouse. The season starts next month,' he replies tersely.

'Really? Why will I want to beat a grouse?' I ask trying to contain my disappointment.

'Where are you frae?' he suddenly asks frowning at me. Well, that's what I think he is doing, his face is so wrinkly and weathered it's difficult to tell.

'New Zealand,' I respond coolly.

'Aye well, you'll be no good then,' he says sourly and stomps off.

Oh shame, I guess that's the end of my career as a grouse murderer. Frankly, I'm not bothered. Wild parties are one thing but walking for miles through the damp undergrowth beating the bushes with a stick to scare some birds into flying out into the path of waiting shotguns isn't really my idea of fun.

JULY

Monday 10th

Today, I relate to Davina an interesting encounter I had in the wine bar in town the previous week. I'd had a week's holiday as a friend was visiting so we went out to check out the night-life. We were home by 9.30. Yep, that exciting. Anyway, we were been sitting at the wine barrel table – oh so last century – when the 2 women sitting next to us suddenly joined in. I think it was my friend. She's not selective who she speaks to. I mentioned I work at Cauldron Manor and one of the women suddenly looked very startled. Rabbit caught in the headlights kind of startled.

'Well I suppose you've heard all about me,' she says rather aggressively. I resist looking at my friend. We'd just had a conversation about narcissists and how I suspect Calis the Conservator might be one. No, I mean a real one. I don't use the term lightly.

'I may have,' I answer cautiously, 'if I knew who you are.'

She says nothing for a minute or two. And then: 'don't tell anyone you've seen me. I'm Rochelle, I used to be the Head Housekeeper at Cauldron Manor until I walked out last winter without giving any of those bitches notice.'

'Did you?' I say. I have heard but I don't say anything. I am, however, desperate to ask why. Oh dear, not such a moral high ground after all. I guess when you spend a lot of time in a gossiping environment it begins to seem less awful. Hyper normalisation I think is the term. A bit like committing the first murder after that it's easier to do the second and, well then after that there's no point feeling righteous about other people's murders. Or indeed murderers.

My lack of response seems to have the desired effect.

'It's because of that bloody Calis the Conservator,' she says taking a large glug of wine. 'She was vile to me and spread all sorts of nasty stories about me. According to her, I was lazy, I didn't do any work, I was a drunk and I came to work drunk. And she told everyone I was shagging all the gardeners! One morning I slipped on some ice on the drawbridge, fell over and broke my arm. She actually walked past me, looked down her nose at me and told Morgan (one of the gardeners) to pick me up and take me home because I was clearly too drunk to work. She later denied it of course but Morgan heard her.'

Ouch.

Note to self. Never underestimate Calis the Conservator.

Davina admits it's probably true.

'Poor Rochelle,' she says, 'she was always in tears. She didn't know how to deal with Calis the Conservator. But you do,' she adds quickly just in case

I'm having second thoughts about working over the winter. I am but I'm keeping it to myself and besides, the only people who have ever mentioned winter work to me have been Davina and Calis the Conservator. Not entirely sure it's going to happen especially when Mrs Upstairs seems to avoid meeting with me.

Wednesday 13th

It is quiet this morning until the rest of the staff arrived. I can feel the change in the atmosphere even though I'm upstairs. When I say a change in atmosphere, I mean the buzz of gossip filtering through to the upstairs rooms seems more intense than usual.

I head downstairs reluctantly. Do I want to hear what this is about? This constant gossiping is wearing but I'm finding it harder and harder not to be pulled into it. I spend some time dusting the ancient flintlock pistols displayed on the landing trying to ignore the murmur of voices drifting up from the front desk. After a while, Davina comes to find me.

'You'll never guess what,' she says as soon as she sees me, 'and don't worry this is not gossip.'

Turns out Mrs Upstairs went mad yesterday because the alarms kept going off. This usually means someone has reached over the ropes into the path of the infrared beams. It happens all the time because the beams are very close to the ropes so sometimes, they can be off by someone's elbow crossing the line. Always seems a little excessive (or paranoid) to me.

The security guards/guides now have to 'patrol' on a constant circuit while Elspeth and Lucinda have to watch the security monitors 'like hawks.' okay but not sure why this has created such a fuss.

Seems everyone is pissed off because yesterday Mrs Upstairs organised some guided tours without bothering to tell anyone. Not only that but she scheduled them all to begin at the same time so there were about 50 people all going through at the same time expecting a detailed, guided tour. If she'd bothered to tell anyone then Colm would have been rostered on to help Rory.

I'm surprised to hear neither get paid extra for these tours although she charges the visitors an extra fifty quid for them but all for her pocket. Anyway, no-one was free to manage security so Mrs Upstairs, who can hear the alarms in her office/bunker, erupted (sounds messy) and marched through all the rooms threatening the visitors with the police if she heard the alarms go off one more time. She was incandescent with rage (now there's an image) and shouted at the visitors demanding to know 'are you're all stupid or something you can't see the alarm beams.' Many people left in disgust. She's told the staff if she sees any bad reviews on TripAdvisor, they will be in serious trouble.

I am slightly anxious at hearing this. Hmm, she's beginning to sound too nutty for my liking.

Friday 14th

This morning I ask Rory about Rochelle but before he can answer Elspeth jumps in and goes off on a rant about how she was lazy, a drunk and sex mad. Rory rolls his eyes at me.

I innocently ask her if she, Elspeth, worked last summer then (I know she didn't. She's been working there for only a couple more weeks than I have)? She has to admit she hadn't and so she's never actually met Rochelle. I had noticed Calis and Elspeth seemed to be getting as thick as thieves. They seem to do an awful lot of whispering together but worryingly, stop whenever I hove into view. Luckily for me, I don't particularly like Elspeth so don't give a toss what she thinks about me.

'So, you don't actually know if any of it's true,' I say but she's not in the least abashed.

'No smoke without fire,' she says glaring at me.

'Well, I guess it depends on who sets the fire,' I reply and walk off quickly to the Housekeepers' Hovel so she won't see my smug smile. As a response, I'm pretty impressed with it. And it came out nowhere.

Reminder to self. Never, never underestimate Calis the Conservator and the power of her malicious gossip.

Monday 17th

Rory doesn't bother to do his usual Gidday practice with me this morning but grabs me by the elbow as soon as I appear and pulls me into the flower room, slamming the door behind him. For a few horrifying minutes, I'm afraid he is going to make a pass at me. I try to think if I've ever encouraged him. I can't imagine his futile attempts to say 'gidday cobber' in a New Zealand accent and my futile attempts to sort out his pronunciation can ever be construed as a kind of flirtation but, hey, if you want to think someone's flirting with you then anything can be construed as such.

'I want to warn you about Elspeth,' Rory breathes in a loud whisper. He's a heavy smoker so it isn't pleasant.

Oh dear. What now?

'She and Calis are as thick as thieves. She's trying to get Lucinda's job.'

'Who? Calis?' Bit confused.

'No, Elspeth.'

'But they have the same job.' A bit more confused.

'Yes, but she wants to work full-time and get rid of Lucinda.'

okay, losing the will to live now.

I try for diplomatic. 'Well don't think it's entirely down to Calis who does what job,' I point out.

'You say that,' Rory hisses intensely keeping his eyes fixed on the glass panel in the door. I guess it's in case anyone comes; anyone like Calis or Elspeth, 'but look how she got rid of Rochelle.'

okay, he may have a point.

AUGUST

Monday 1st

I arrive this morning to find the carpets are dirty enough to plant seedlings in. Seems it was a busy weekend and all set to be busier than ever today. To be fair it is a summer bank holiday. Back home, we'd be chilling the Savignon Blanc, covering ourselves head to toe in Factor 30 and heading to the beach or firing up the barbie to make the most of the sun; and the holiday. Odd how people here think a good day out is traipsing through someone else's dark house. But I guess no odder than sucking up to the aristocracy. Seems a lot of people come in the hope of catching a glimpse of Mrs Upstairs. I wonder if they're disappointed by her.

I am upstairs doing a bit of dusting in the Portrait Gallery. It's a grim place this Portrait Gallery. Full of morose characters all looking down their noses at me. They are, I must say a pretty ugly lot; big noses, thin lips, poppy eyes. But I guess the gene pool was pretty small back in the day since they tried to keep the line pure by not getting entangled with any common blood. Pure! Ha, what a laugh! I suspect there's a spot of madness in their 'pure' DNA as there appear to be a few murders of heirs usually committed by the nearest and dearest, often the wife. Ouch.

I'm halfway through the dusting and glaring at the 14th century Duke because I find him even more obnoxious than most (he organised his daughter's marriage to the next-door Baron by getting him to rape her... not nice and not the kind of dad I'd ever want) when I'm aware there's someone else in the room. For a nanosecond, I'm a bit freaked thinking it might be his ghost come to settle a score with me and my feminist hatred but no, it's a very beautiful young woman, who is staring at a portrait of the latest late Duke. I can't work out if she's real or not because a) we're not open to the public yet and b) I didn't hear her coming into the room. I just turned and there she was.

'Hello,' she says, 'sorry if I frightened you but I'm Lady Philippa.' She says this as if I should know who she is. Nope, not ringing any bells.

'How did you get in here?' I ask cautiously.

'Oh, Lucinda always lets me in a bit early before all the visitors arrive and before my stepmother's had her breakfast up at The House so there's no chance we will ever run into each other. As far as she's concerned, I'm only allowed in if I pay.'

Ah, ha bells are ringing.

Turns out she's the youngest daughter of the late Duke. Four sons; that's an heir and 3 spares, and two daughters. None of them is allowed to enter without Mrs Upstairs' express permission or without paying. Seems to bit much to have to pay to see your childhood home. It doesn't surprise me Lucinda lets her in. Lucinda doesn't say too much about the current Dowager Duchess but her expression whenever she's mentioned speak volumes. I've also worked out she's no fan of Calis the Conservator who it seems 'sucks up' to the Dowager Duchess 'like there's no tomorrow'.

I guess when it comes down to it, most of the staff are probably genetically programmed to feel for the hereditary family since their families have all worked for them since the beginning of time. And Mrs Upstairs is an American interloper.

Lady Philippa tells me her mother's portrait used to hang in the spot where the current Dowager Duchess's now resides. Seems a bit mean when according to the bits of gossip I can't avoid hearing, this current Dowager was the final straw that broke up the Duke's first marriage. 2 weeks after the divorce, they married. What's she got to feel aggrieved about? Maybe it's guilt?

Anyway, I've come to the conclusion the artist was either very short-sighted or she paid him over the odds to portray her looking small, slim and ethereal; none of these adjectives I suspect really apply to her. True, I've never seen her so can't really comment but even the best cover-up jobs can't hide the big teeth and hair. Not a good combo.

She then shows me the portrait of her mother, the late Duke's first wife has been moved to a spot on the wall behind the door so when the door is open, she's invisible. Her mother is beautiful (I say 'is' because she's still around). Oh well, her genes must have improved the general unappealing-ness of the family because Lady Philippa is beautiful. I wonder what the current Duke looks like since the late one was no oil painting.

Tuesday 2nd

I hear Mrs Upstairs completely lost her rag yesterday.

Again.

I'm deeply disappointed I missed it.

Again.

Is this perhaps the 'she'll go mad' thing Calis the Conservator is always threatening?

It was very busy with a long line of people waiting to come in. The Dowager, it seems, showed her common roots by shouting at everyone no more than 30 people are allowed through at any one time because the Manor wouldn't take it. It's been standing for 700 odd years so not sure how that works. She even pulled staff out of the cafe, despite them being completely rushed off their feet, and insisted they guard the drawbridge and prevent people from entering. Well, the public pay £15 odd to get in, which I think is outrageous and a bit greedy since the cafe is also really expensive and not particularly good quality but I suppose she has to pay for her holidays somehow, but not sure you can stop people entering when they've paid their entrance fee.

Luckily, for everyone and the public, Mrs Upstairs always goes back up to The House for lunch at 1 pm so to a man/woman, the staff heaved a sigh of relief and left the visitors to get on with their visiting. Manfred, her chef, promised to phone down if, when she'd finished snuffling in her trough, she decided to return to create more mayhem but since, according to Davina, who should know because she's usually still there cleaning up after her, Mrs Upstairs tends to flop out on the couch eating chocs after luncheon, the chances of her popping back are fairly small.

Monday 8th

Davina and I are putting the cleaning equipment (I use the term loosely: a few dusters made from someone's old tee-shirts and the heavier than hell vacuum cleaners) in the cupboard in the Housekeepers' Hovel when Ivo struts down with Caitlin. I try really hard not to dislike him but it's difficult. I can't work out if Caitlin is completely taken in by him or she's just being careful. Either way, I keep my thoughts to myself but it's impossible not to hear everyone else moaning about him.

'Don't go,' he instructs without looking at either of us as he swaggers self-importantly past us into the vestibule.

He and Caitlin are about to 'inspect' our work. Well, I guess there's a first time for everything. 'Wait here until we return,' he commands. I think he was trying for authoritative but his squeaky voice kind of killed the effect.

Davina mouths 'what the feck' to me then stalks off to the Housekeepers' Hovel breathing fire. I follow her down the ramp.

Something's going on, she points out because whenever we ask Ivo to do anything to make our job easier or quicker, he always passes the buck supremely and says housekeeping is not his domain.

'He's the fecking General Manager! How is it not his domain?' Well, apparently now it is his domain.

'He's nothing but a fecking waste of air,' she throws over her shoulder to me as she heads for the door. She gets a telling off from Mrs Upstairs if she's not up at the summer House by 10.15.

Ivo reappears and gives me a list (pathetically small and definitely stretching it. Anything, I guess to make himself feel important) of things we've missed. I tell him Davina had to go and I'll do it tomorrow. He doesn't know how to respond but then says something that leaves me open mouthed (seriously, not often someone can catch me out like that).

'Never mind, Caitlin or I will do it. We often do the things you've missed when we do our daily morning inspection.'

I am truly astonished at such a bald-faced lie. He never inspects. He barely bothers to come into the Manor except when he wants to show off to someone or he needs an ego stroke.

Note to self: he's up to something or something is up. Be alert.

Tuesday 9th

I arrive this morning to find Davina in full gripe mode with Miserable Murdo about Ivo.

'I don't care if I'm gossiping,' she says following me up the stairs. 'He's a wee shite.' She's clearly still angry with him. 'And don't you go trusting him,' she instructs, 'the only person he cares about is himself and the only person he looks out for is himself and his wee girl gang up there in the office.'

I don't say anything but I know she's right. More and more I'm becoming uneasy with the gossiping and hypocrisy in this place. All looks lovely on the outside but inside, it feels like I'm hovering on the edge of a viper pit.

Or maybe I just need a holiday.

Saturday 13th

Have just been told by Caitlin that Jodie the Joyless is back. What! Really? Jodie walked out. What are they thinking? She's only working Sundays because as I'm on my own, Caitlin feels I need help as I usually have to head up to one or both holiday cottages to clean them out for the changeover. I can see her point but Jodie? Really?

Sunday 14th

It is a grim day today. Jodie the Joyless doesn't speak to me, only glares. She mutters something about 'workmates telling tales on other workmates'. Not sure what her beef is but seriously not interested. As long as she does her job, it does take the pressure off me since I am struggling a bit with Sundays.

She does stick around vacuuming until 10 but Colm the ex-cop tells me, she sat in the library reading a book for an hour before she started work. He saw her on the CCTV (I'm always acutely aware of the CCTV. Odd how my Catholic guilt always flips on whenever I'm aware of them). I guess she's cutting her hour from the other end now. Not much I can say but if nothing else, the upstairs carpet gets vacuumed and not by me.

Monday 15th

Davina does a little rant and an angry dance when I tell her Jodie the Joyless is back on the scene. Caitlin comes down while she's in the middle of this and Davina demands to know why we have to put up with the lazy gripe when we work our socks off and she does as little as possible.

Caitlin points out she did come down at 9.30 and saw how Jodie was still working. I decide not to go there with the 'she sat in the library doing nothing for the first hour'. No point. I think they're just desperate for staff and Jodie was available.

Davina goes off to complain to Calis the Conservator though I'm not sure what she can do about it. I think Davina has more faith in The Conservator than she actually deserves. Calis is someone who is very good at bigging themselves up so they can appear much more important than they really are. I also think Calis and Jodie hate each other because they are similar personalities.

The Clash of the Narcissists.

When Davina reports back it is to say The Conservator said the Dowager 'would go mad,' if she ever found out. Not entirely sure how useful that is but Davina seems placated.

Wednesday 17th

I arrive back after my now one-day-a-week-off and Davina, red with rage, tells me Jodie has decided she also wants to work Mondays which is one of the days I work. I tell her to calm down. Frankly, I'm a bit over it all. I'm not prepared to stop working Mondays and if Davina doesn't want to either, then I'm guessing there's not a lot upstairs can do about. After all, why should we have to change just to suit Jodie the Joyless? It's not like she's a valued member of the team.

I point this out to Caitlin who is looking seriously stressed. She's just been on the phone with Mrs

Upstairs who has told her she thinks Davina and I are lazy and not working hard enough. I am shocked by this. I know I work hard and try to do my job as well as possible. Anyway, how would she know as she never comes inside the Manor but just lurks menacingly in her bunker by the front entrance. She's also made no attempt to meet me though it's been threatened often enough. I think of the times I've hung around waiting to meet her only to find, she's got better things to do. I now feel no guilt about filling her filtered water jug with water from the toilet handbasin. I decide from now on to use water from the actual toilet.

I tell Caitlin not to worry, she probably hasn't had her breakfast yet and some people just can't cope with low blood sugar.

Still, all this for minimum wages. Really?

Saturday 20th

Ivo pops down surrounded by his usual ego-cloud and spends several minutes telling me how great he is at this job and how great he was at his last one, and the one before that and the one before that. I interrupt to point out I'm on my own and I've still got upstairs to do before opening. I distrust him more and more. It's not comfortable feeling like this but I find myself wondering what he's after. He never does anything without a reason. I wonder what his agenda today is.

Turns out, he's come to tell me Jodie the Joyless is going to help me with the holiday cottages. I tell me if she wants to clean them, then she can do them on her own. I'm not going anywhere isolated with that mad woman. Who knows what she'll do to me when we're on our own and besides, I know she won't do any work so there's no point. Ivo looks affronted but I just walk off. He can deal with his affrontedness by himself. Not my problem.

Ivo catches me just as I'm leaving and says really coldly (I guess my walking off and leaving him affronted has really... affronted him) there's no change-over this weekend, so it isn't an issue but we will discuss it next week. I tell him not to bother, either she does them on her own or I do. Simple as.

Sunday 21st

Jodie does her usual sitting in the Library reading a magazine until 9 when she deigns to emerge to start work. Unfortunately for her, there is a big coach party booked in at 9.30 and she is nowhere close to finishing the vacuuming.

Ivo comes down slightly panicked and looking for someone to blame for his panicked feeling. He tells us we need to get a move on as the party has already arrived and while they are busy in the gardens at the moment, they'll want to come into the Manor soon.

Jodie throws her vacuum cleaner hose on the floor and has a hissy fit, ranting about how just because we are the plebs (speak for yourself. A pleb I am not!), we should still be told when there's a coach party coming in so we can be finished on time. Ivo looks at me. Oh, interesting. He's asking for my help since Jodie is spitting venom.

I point out there is a list of coach parties with expected times of arrival left on the desk by the front door and surely, she's been around long enough to know to look. And really, if only she started work at the proper time, then she'd be finished by now. Luckily, she was too busy ranting to take in what I'd just said. Though no doubt it will sink in eventually.

Ivo asks me pleadingly if I can help her finish because time is running out. The coach party is already hovering at the door and peering with increasing agitation through the glass. Lucinda is freaking out but handling it well. There must be about 50 people out there. She goes to the door and points out it's not 9.30 yet and they have to give housekeeping time to do their job properly. She orders them back to the gardens.

Impressed.

They do as she instructs and even she looks surprised.

Ivo is still looking hopefully at me. I agree but as I walk past him and mutter, 'holiday cottages.' He rolls his eyes but I think I made my point.

As we've had to finish at 9.30, though Jodie the Joyless probably worked less than one hour, I see she's making up time by gossiping with Susie in the Gift Shop. I am not fond of Susie and avoid her when possible. She does weird things like appearing at the front desk when we are all trying to finish getting ready to open, asking stupid questions and storming off when no one has time to stop to talk to her. She's is a victim par excellence. And a gossiper without competition. Her latest gossip is to claim Ivo and June from accounts are having an affair. This is dangerous because both are married and there's no evidence. And besides, even if they are, it's no one's business but theirs and she should keep her nose out and not repeat it as if it is the truth.

I walk past the Gift Shop and both Jodie and Susie stop to glare at me. I wonder what they are saying but then I remind myself I actually don't care. Both are passive/aggressive nut jobs.

This Manor House, I decide, may look impressive and lovely on the outside but on the inside, it's definitely turning out to be something less than lovely. I'm trying not to be disappointed by this. The only part of the job I really enjoy is the walk up the curved driveway towards the drawbridge in the early morning when it's all quiet and peaceful and sometimes there's a little bit of mist hovering over the lawns.

This morning I go up to the Manor really early long and before anyone is due to start work. I enjoy the peace while watching the day come to life. I make sure

I stay on the side where the gardens are so I don't alert Davina's brother, who's security and sleeps on the premises at night, to my presence. It is really beautiful this early in the day. To my surprise, I see an elderly man raking in one of the flower beds. I've never seen him before but that's not unusual, there are quite a few people who work on the Estate whom I've never seen before. Still he's awfully early and I'm a bit cross because I was looking forward to a bit of peace and quiet before all the moaning, miserable, gossiping people start work.

Still, he's taking no notice of me so I figure I can ignore him back. Besides he's a little way off in the thick of the gardens and I can't hear him so I sit out my quiet time.

Later, when I'm leaving, I run into my gardener friend. We do the banter bit and I laugh at his Kiwi accent while he laughs at my Scottish one. When I mention the elderly gardener, I saw earlier in the morning and comment about his early start, he has no idea who I'm talking about. He's the oldest gardener there.

I don't know what to say. I'm a bit disturbed.

'Ghost,' he says and laughs, 'there's plenty about.'

Not sure how to take this but hey if he was a ghost, he seemed harmless enough but somehow the thought of sitting in the garden first thing in the morning has lost its appeal.

Tuesday 23rd

When I arrive at work today, I see Davina is in the Gift Shop and has her head down with Susie and both are looking intense. What is it with Susie and that Gift Shop? A gossip hub possibly.

I'm upstairs dusting and checking for mouse poo, I'm gratified to see the culprit has evaded capture and is pooing for Scotland. There's mouse poo all up the curtains now. When Davina tracks me down, she is so intent telling me her bit of news, she barely glances as I point at the mouse lavatory cluttering up the curtains.

Susie had told her Ivo and June are having an affair and it's official because Susie has seen them. Oh god, I'm seriously sick of this. Gossip can be dangerous. I know because I had a business competitor who pretended to be my friend but told lies about me to all her customers, some of whom were also mine which affected my business quite substantially. It took me two years to knock it on the head.

I ask her in what way did Susie see them? I mean did she witness then in a sexual clinch. Davina seems a bit flummoxed at this and has to admit, no Susie just saw them standing with their heads very close together, having an intense conversation.

'What? Just like you and Susie were a few minutes ago,' I say. 'Are you two having an affair then?'

Davina is not pleased and stalks off. I'm a bit upset because I really like Davina, she's a good ally so I don't want her to be cross with me but I wish she'd be a bit more circumspect about what people tell her.

Later, in the Housekeepers' Hovel, she tells me how cross she is with herself for getting sucked in again. I tell her not to worry because serious, serial gossips are really good at it. It's an art they've practised for years. I remind her not to believe anything unless she's witnessed it for herself. And imagine if either Ivo or June's other halves heard that stuff. It could have nasty repercussions.

You are so wise, she says. I walk to my car barely able to contain my smugness. I'm normal. I can be vain.

Friday 26th

Fenella the cafe manager with whom I have a nice little rapport (I suck up to her and she gives me free coffee) gives me a scone with cream and jam today because she's just found about Joyless. It seems they had a run-in in the past. Joyless decided she could run the cafe and expected to be given the job because she asked for it and then did everything possible to get Fenella the sack. She joins me with a scone and coffee while we silently commiserate on the sheer delusional nuttiness of it all.

I had for some time harboured under the illusion I could no longer be surprised by the actions of people. Not so sure now.

SEPTEMBER

Sunday 4th

Joyless turns up late this morning. I'm hiding out sweeping the dungeon steps with my head low so she can't see me unless she specifically looks for me. I doubt she'll want to see me because that would mean engaging with me and since I'm the 'bitch' who took her hours, I doubt she will bother.

Wrong.

She suddenly appears at the top of the steps so silently, I jump about 10 feet and screech. No, she doesn't look that bad but she was so silent and I was so intent on staying invisible, I didn't see her until she was suddenly there.

She looks down her nose at me. I stand up and walk away before she has a chance to say whatever it is she wants to say to me. I don't want to encourage her to engage with me any more than I can stand. I don't like the fact I'm a bit scared of her.

She calls after me to tell me she has to leave early because her husband can't look after their children. I don't bother to ask why or why she's bothered to make up this excuse when she always leaves early. Or starts late.

Elspeth, I've noticed is getting increasingly cosy with Calis. This makes me increasingly uneasy. Calis shouldn't even be here on a Sunday. When I ask her why she says she hates not being at work. It's so boring for her at home. I'm sure her husband and children must be overjoyed to hear that. On the other hand, they probably are overjoyed.

Small mercies, silver linings and every cloud.

Monday 5th

Mrs Upstairs is away. Again. How hard we all work so she can enjoy her little sojourns. She's gone to Nairobi to visit her son.

Davina tells me he's probably in trouble with the authorities again since that's the only time Mrs Upstairs goes to visit him. Davina doesn't care. It means she doesn't have to go up to The House to clean it though I see Calis is pretty annoyed when Davina tells her she's not going. Calis does a bit of drama queening about how much cleaning there is to do. Davina, I'm pleased to note stands her ground even if she does try to justify it by saying she's not feeling well.

'Would you like me to help?' I ask safe in the knowledge that as The Conservator has grown increasingly antipathetic towards me (not sure why but not sure I care) and makes little attempt to hide it, I suspect she would probably rather stick a pen in her eye than go anywhere with me. And besides, how can she dramatise how busy she is if someone is there to see how busy she isn't.

Tuesday 6th

Calis has obviously been complaining to Morbidly Miserable Murdo. When he sits down on the stairs by the front desk for his usual morning whinge, he goes on and on about all the work Calis had to do by herself up at The House yesterday. She was there until 9 pm apparently. Oh well, no doubt that was a relief for her family.

I comment in all apparent innocence how I'd offered to go up to help her but she turned down my offer. He looks a bit put out at this. No doubt, this was a piece of information The Conservator had forgotten to pass on to him.

'It's specialised,' he splutters, 'you probably wouldn't have been any use.'

I turn to Davina and ask her how specialised it is. She shrugs and says, 'it's just cleaning. Anyone could do it.' At this, Miserable Murdo stomps off looking really miserable. Davina high fives me.

'Specialised my arse,' she says rolling her eyes. I warm to her daily.

Friday 9th

The Dowager's son has been arrested and charged with ivory smuggling. I hate him already though I know I should not make a judgement without seeing the evidence first. She's paid his bail equivalent to several hundred thousand pounds. Oh well, I guess the saving she's made on paying me minimum wages has contributed to that.

It's in all the papers. All of them.

Davina tells me this means The Manor will probably be really busy tomorrow with visitors. Not sure why since he doesn't live here and Mrs Upstairs is away. Anyway, it makes no odds to me since I have to vacuum the carpet irrespective of how dirty it actually is …or isn't. Vacuuming is vacuuming is vacuuming.

Monday 12th

Elspeth shows me an article from a Sunday Newspaper documenting the Ivory Smuggling Scheme Mrs Upstairs' son is supposed to be involved in. He's pleading his innocence. He looks very harried and not nearly so languid in the newspaper photo but no doubt it was chosen for precisely that reason. He's referred to as a 'playboy' and the stepbrother of the Duke. Naturally, the Duke and his family, all of them even the grandchildren are distancing themselves with what almost looks indecent haste.

Their statement in the papers: 'He's not related to us and we've little contact with him since his mother only married our father when we were adults and no longer lived at home.' The inference is they probably wouldn't recognise him if they sat next to him.

Mrs Upstairs claims he is being 'victimised' because of his 'connections'. According to her, some people can't deal with the fact there are those in the world who are just better than they are and will do everything in their power to bring them down. The implication is; it's a class thing and the lower classes are jealous. And spiteful.

Wednesday 13th

While Mrs Upstairs is so publicly away in Nairobi, some of the late Duke's estranged family come for a visit bringing their children to have a look around the family pile. They are let in free and there's an awful lot of cap doffing and forelock tugging in their presence.

I notice they manage to melt away whenever Calis the Conservator or Morbidly Moaning Murdo hove into sight. I guess there's the worry those two may report back to Mrs Upstairs and everyone's job will be on the line. I wonder if they post look-outs to relay reports on Calis and Miserable Murdo's whereabouts and movements because unless everyone is suddenly psychic, they seem remarkably prescient about either's imminent arrival. I notice Ivo and Caitlin stay out of the way. I guess it's a case of 'didn't see so don't know'.

Wednesday 20th

Well, I suspect she paid whoever it is you pay off, off. Mrs Upstairs' son has been released without charge on the condition he quits the country. He's heading off to family in the States while Mrs Upstairs is on her way back. Damn. It is actually pleasant, her being away and with the visits from the late Duke's children. Even the late Dukes ex-wife turned up for afternoon tea in the café. Missed her I'm afraid. She came after I'd left but everyone who saw her gushes about what a 'lady' she is. She left the staff a few bottles of bubbly to enjoy a drink on her.

A lady with style. Mrs Upstairs could learn a few things from her I feel.

Monday 25th

Two things happened today. Joyless finally left completely which makes no difference to anything or anyone as she hasn't been able to work her last couple of shifts. No point her being here then. And Mrs Upstairs is back. Everyone is very careful. And no one mentions the late Duke's children visiting. It's as if it never happened. Odd how everyone has pulled together to keep that little secret though no doubt someone will slip up and let it out. Susie probably though she's got other things on her mind. And as she's so focused on herself she's probably oblivious to anything going on around her which doesn't actually involve her. She's building up for some drama. I can see it in the frenzy of gossip going on around her. Davina looks harried. I feel sorry for her.

I discover, later in the morning, accompanying Mrs Upstairs to her summer estate is none other than her Ivory Smuggling Son. He's decided to stop off for a short visit to check out the Manor House before he wends his smuggling way back to the States. Perhaps he's reasserting his place in the family's pecking order, which from all accounts, is pretty low down.

'She could leave it to him.' I hear Rory telling Elspeth, 'Cauldron Manor, if the young Duke keeps pissing her off in the way he has been, there's a good chance she will.'

'Never!' Elspeth screeches loudly enough to disturb the bats in the belfry (yes, there is one and it has bats. Not making it up), 'whatever else she is, or was, she'd never sully the memory of her late husband like that. And besides, she's only allowed to live in it while she's alive.'

'Aye well,' Rory tuts, 'none of us know that for sure.' I peer around the wall from the bottom of the stairs to catch him giving her a knowing nod. How is it, people who know nothing always manage those knowing nods?

I'm half way up the stairs before I hear him. The son. A loud, posh voice with an odd American type twang. Do I want to see him? Do I want to meet him?

Yes, no, yes no, I'm busy tossing it up when I hear him order Elspeth to fetch how a cawfee and a maid or something because his boots need polishing.

Oh, that'll be a No then.

I scuttle up the stairs to hide out in the Long Gallery.

Later on, when I'm leaving, I see him lurking by Mrs Upstairs's office/bunker door. I can only say, though to be fair, my glance at him as I picked up my pace over the drawbridge was pretty cursory as I didn't want him to get any ideas about getting his boots polished, his portrait in Mrs Upstairs's office is very complimentary. It occurs to me, perhaps the portrait in her office/bunker isn't of him after all.

Tuesday 26th

The gift shop is closed for most of the morning. As I'm leaving, I see Caitlin standing in there looking busy. She looks at me through the window, shakes her head and rolls her eyes. There's drama in the air. I wonder where Susie is since she treats the Gift Shop as if it's her own personal domain. If it weren't for the fact, I see her arriving in the morning, I'd suspect she slept in there. I'm tempted to pop in to ask Caitlin what's going on but resist the urge. I have to admit it, sometimes the moral high ground can be a lonely place. Besides, I remind myself, Davina will no doubt will tell me all about it eventually since she's in so thick with Susie. I know they meet up for lunch sometimes.

Wednesday 27th

Davina's day off today but the air is heavy with a kind of frenzy. Rory and Elspeth are muttering by the flower room and there's a lot of head nodding, knowing looks and teeth sucking going on. As I'm on my own, I ignore it to get on with the vacuuming and dusting. I suspect it's something to do with Susie and knowing the propensity for gossip in this place, I'm pretty confident I'll get hear about it eventually whether I want to or not.

Working upstairs on my own is peaceful except when I'm dusting the ancestors. Being in there with them makes me grumpy. I decide to do a skim dust. I do this by running the feather duster under their noses. When I leave, I imagine them all sneezing furiously.

Small pleasures.

OCTOBER

Monday 3rd

Today, surprise, surprise, I actually finally get to meet Mrs Upstairs. Not a planned meeting but an accidental one. I climb to the tower office and inadvertently walk in on a meeting between Caitlin, Ivo, Susie one of the shop assistants and another person who I can only surmise is Susie's legal or union rep. I went in because I want to return the keys of one of the cottages I'd been cleaning.

There's been a bit of a drama building over the last few days between Susie, Ivo and Caitlin. I've overheard, on a couple of occasions, Susie and Calis the Conservator whispering together in the staff room, which, unfortunately for everyone who works at the Manor, just happens to be right next to Calis the Conservator's lair and, conveniently for her, from where she can hear pretty much everything anyone says. I begin to understand how useful she must be to Mrs Upstairs.

One way to keep your finger on the pulse.

Yesterday morning, I hear Calis the Conservator telling Susie she has to watch Ivo and Caitlin because they are trying to get rid of her. Susie is getting upset and crying. I wish I have to courage to tell Calis the Conservator to shut up. I can tell from her voice she's enjoying herself so there's something uncomfortably manipulative about this interaction. She's spent quite a bit of time over the first few months trying to get me to take sides in the Ivo/Caitlin thing but when she realised I wasn't playing ball, she pretty much stopped speaking to me. Phew. I'm still syrupy nice to her and I enjoy knowing she thinks I'm a bit stupid.

As I walk away from the staff room back down the dim corridor in what used to be the servant's area, (there is still the board with bells labelled with things like: Duke's bedroom, Duchess's bedroom, Drawing Room, Breakfast room – you get the idea) Susie comes out of the staff room, sees me and chases after me.

'Did you hear that?' She asks pushing past and stopping in front of me so I can't keep walking.

'Hear what?' I ask trying to side step her but either she's done a lot of dancing or she's practised at this, I can't dodge her. I really don't want to encourage her. I don't particularly like her.

'Ivo and Caitlin are trying to get rid of me. They took my CD player out of the shop yesterday. How am I supposed to sell CDs if I can't play them for customers?' She's all breathless and high pitched, almost screeching.

Not sure how to answer that. Not sure it's even a rational statement.

'Oh dear,' I say as innocuously as I can manage. I really don't want to talk about it but can't quite bring myself to tell her I'm not interested. It's all too nutty for me.

'Calis also overheard Ivo and Cassie talking about how they can get rid of me.'

Now I actually doubt this is true. Cassie is into all things spiritual and is a Medium and Healer. We often find each other and talk about things other than the Manor, other staff or Mrs Upstairs. It gets her down a bit too, all the moaning and gossiping.

'Why would they want to get rid of you?' I ask patiently. Susie is only summer staff. She barely works 5 months of the year but I suddenly I do begin wonder if it's anything to do with her spreading rumours about Ivo and June from accounts.' Anyway, it's nearly the end of the season,' I tell her. 'Why would they wait till now?

'Because I've worked here for years,' she says and starts to cry. 'They just want all us older ones out so they can bring in new staff. Make a clean sweep and have everything running the way they want it.'

'I really don't think so,' I try to remain calm but she's in floods of tears now and I'm feeling really pissed off with Calis the Conservator who has no doubt stirred this up because it sounds exactly like the propaganda she spouts. And besides Ivo and Caitlin are in charge, they can run the place any way they want and staff just have to do as they're told irrespective of how new or old, they are. 'If that's really been the case, I doubt they would've got you back to work here for this season.'

She stops to think about this for a minute but I can see she doesn't want to agree with it. Nothing like being a victim enjoying the drama.

If Ivo and Caitlin do want to get rid of her, then she's offered them the perfect opportunity because I'm later told by Rory, how she threw an enormous tantrum after finding her CD player had been removed (it's not hers, it belongs to the shop but she's very possessive about that shop and all its contents) before storming off and leaving the shop unattended. Davina found her sobbing hysterically in the car-park, which seems like a bit of an overreaction for not being able to play naff CDs. Personally, I'd be relieved. Playing watery music all day isn't my idea of fun.

I think she's hard work.

I later hear Calis the Conservator gossiping to Elspeth about how unstable Susie is.

Yep, see nasty and two-faced. Susie's apparently asked Calis the Conservator for her mobile number because she'd like to see her outside work but Calis is not going to give it to her. Calis the Conservator gives no one her mobile number. Only people she likes. She told me this with pride. And since she won't give it to me (I dared to ask for it once), I take it she doesn't like me. Though it's becoming pretty obvious. I think I've interrupted her on a couple of occasions whining about me. I feel pretty confident she doesn't like Susie either but enjoys manipulating her for her own ends.

Oh, I see very clearly how manipulative she is.

Note to self: who would I trust more?

Viper or Calis the Conservator? Viper or Calis the Conservator?

Viper of course. No contest. Don't even know why I'm pretending it is a contest.

Anyway, after accidentally interrupting their meeting in the Tower Office during which time I suggest patronisingly, they lock the door downstairs (that way I can blame them for my interrupting them... if you get my drift), I head down to the other office next to Mrs Upstairs' office/bunker when she opens her just door as I step through the door.

'Oh hi,' I say when she glares at me. I give her my name.

'Oh. How do you do?' She says looking me up and down before, to my surprise, shaking my hand. Her hand is soft and cool. I am pleased I'm dressed rather flamboyantly because I'm not into ageing gracefully or beige-ly which clearly, she is. Her accent is a weird mix of posh and American so there's a bit of a clash going on. She also had enormous teeth. I force myself to stop looking.

I have to say she is a bit of a disappointment. Not sure what I was expecting but it is more than that.

Monday 10th

Three weeks until the Manor closes. Already there's a kind of ghost town feeling about the place.

Many of the summer staff have already left to return to university or school or their gardens or whatever. Ivo asks me if I will consider working in the shop for the next three weeks. I'm tempted but it means being in close proximity to Susie who, since her meeting in the office (the one I interrupted), looks permanently aggrieved and spends her days sitting behind her counter looking mournfully out the window at the café customers sitting at the tables in the courtyard. I consider it for a nanosecond but pretend to give it a few more because I don't want to offend him, before declining.

I've decided I've had enough of miserable people. I've had to put up with Morbidly Moaning Murdo's company whenever he drives me up to clean the holiday cottages. Impaling myself on the spikes in the wrought iron gate is beginning to have more appeal. Thankfully, Calis the Conservator no longer speaks to me except to make snide comments which I always pretend are serious and answer accordingly. I see she thinks I'm really stupid but I've got a little 'how to identify a workplace narcissist' checklist going on inside my head. She seems to be ticking an awful lot of the boxes.

Tuesday 11th

Today, Ivo tells us the Dowager thoroughly inspected the Manor the previous evening as part of her preparations for taking up residence again when it finally closes to the public. There are, it seems, many things aren't being done properly and, thus, need rectifying. He glares at me while saying this so I suspect he's paying me back for not taking on the shop job because now he has to do it. I've seen him in there over the last couple of days looking as miserable as Susie and as morbid as Miserable Murdo. Maybe that's what working in this place does for people.

He marches us around the route pointing out this and that but most of it seems pretty minor. And some of it doesn't exist.

'This bowl,' he says running his hand around it, 'is filthy.' It's not, so his hand comes up clean. I say nothing. Never rile an embarrassed man. It could have unintentional consequences and whatever I might think personally about him, he's also mentioned the possibility of my staying on over the winter so I don't want to alienate him.

As punishment, he makes us polish the ancient floorboards in the Long Drawing Room (not to be confused with the Short Drawing Room though why anyone needs two is beyond me) on our hands and knees which is interesting because the Manor is now open and visitors are standing around watching us. Davina and I put on fake cockney accents and pretend we're housemaids. Not sure how authentic the cockney accents manage to sound since I'm a New Zealander and she's Scottish but as most of the visitors are

American, they seem pretty convinced. Well, I suppose no one's could be as bad as Dick Van Dyke's cockney accent in the Mary Poppins film. I like to think ours are better.

'How often do you have to do this?' One visitor asks.

'Everyday, duck,' Davina says. I can tell she's enjoying herself.

Then everyone else begins to ask questions. You can tell they've all to a man/woman watched Downton Abbey. We just go along with it and a few of them actually give us tips.

Monetary ones I mean, not verbal ones.

Nice.

Unfortunately, the fun is short-lived because Ivo reappears. He glowers at us, gives the growing crowd around us a thin smile and says the Dowager Duchess is waiting for both of us at The House.

All the Americans are loudly impressed by this. I hear the words 'the Dowager Duchess' repeated up and down the queue in suitably impressed and sepulchral tones.

Oh, long live the class system.

Then I register what he's said. 'Both of us?' I am confused.

'Yes both,' he snaps. Davina turns and winks at me. I guess this is significant.

Davina drives us up to The House while giving me a quick run-down on what the job entails. She's excited because she thinks this means I'm staying over the winter. I'll wait until I'm asked before I get excited.

We are met by Mrs Upstairs who is cross because we are late. Davina tries to explain about having to polish the floorboards in the Long Drawing Room but she cuts her off short and tells her in harsh peremptory tones to get on with making up the fire in the Library and to make sure she doesn't use quite so much paper as she did yesterday.

'I nearly singed my eyebrows,' she barks to Davina's retreating back. I can tell Davina's cross just from the way she walks.

She then proceeds to take me on a tour of the house to show me exactly and in great detail, what needs to be done. I wonder if she realises there's only the two of us. Gone are the days of maids galore cleaning up after the posh toffs, but clearly, the attitude of the posh toffs remains.

'You must pay attention to detail,' she barks repeatedly. I'm trying to work out what's wrong with her accent until I realise she's somehow strangling every vowel before they can escape from her mouth.

'No worries, Happy to give it a burl,' I say loudly in my exaggerated New Zealand accent. She gives me a suspicious look so I wonder briefly, if I'm hamming it up too much but I'm a bit cross at how rude she was to Davina. I am beginning to understand why Davina is so keen for me to work over the winter.

I finally get to meet Manfred her chef. I've heard a lot about him. Mostly from Calis the Conservator and mostly it was negative things. I do wonder, if she feels it's okay to say the things she does about him and he's a friend, then what the hell does she say about me?

Later, while I'm in the kitchen washing Mrs Upstairs' breakfast dishes (all gently and by hand and don't let the silverware sit in the water or it will come unglued – really? Not good quality then) I tell Manfred a long story about my great-great-great grandfather who was transported to Australia for robbing an aristocrat and killing his wife. It's not true of course. I'm a second-generation New Zealander which is subtly different mostly because it was to Australia, not New Zealand that convicts were sent, and my grandfather emigrated from Ireland of his own free will but I know Mrs Upstairs is sitting in the next room listening to our conversation (Manfred silently warned me when I brought the dishes through) so I'm making sure it's an enjoyable story. Or maybe I'm trying to put the wind up her. Manfred is grinning at me and trying not to laugh out loud so I think we might get on all right though I don't forget he is a good friend of Calis the Conservator's so I reserve judgement.

'I'll see you both here tomorrow at 10 sharp.' Mrs Upstairs tells us imperiously when we finish. Though I'm not sure how we'll manage since we don't finish at the Manor until 10.

'Ignore her,' Davina says, 'she's just pissed off because we were late and now, she has to pay the two of us for an extra half hour.' Right. Well, at minimum wage it works out to be less than 4 pounds for me. What can I say? I guess that's why she's rich and I'm not.

Wednesday 12th

'Come here,' Mrs Upstairs crooks her chubby talon and beckons me upstairs. I hear Davina muttering a 'good luck' as I move past her.

'In here.' Mrs Upstairs stands in the doorway to her bathroom. 'This toilet bowl,' she says pointing at said toilet bowl, 'is not clean.'

I glance down following the direction of her pointing finger. Not sure what to say really. I mean it's nothing to do with me what she chooses to do in her private toilet.

'Now get some salt and vinegar and give it a proper scrub. I want you to get right down inside the bend down there.'

Salt and vinegar! What the hell is she talking about? I wonder briefly if a switch has flipped in my brain and while I hear 'toilet', she's actually saying fish and chips. Or perhaps it's her accent. Or perhaps she's madder than I realise.

Then she tells me, with an air of complacent 'I am so on the moral high ground' smugness, how the use of chemicals is abhorrent to her. She is a firm believer in caring for the environment and 'does everything in her power to adhere to the use of environmentally friendly cleaning agents'.

Yep, good sentiment but not sure I believe her. Her toilet paper is not recycled and is of the expensive, quilted and scented variety. Also, I wonder if she realises vinegar is actually a chemical.

'Salt and vinegar,' I mutter to Davina when I finally find her huddled out of sight in a little nook in the library reading the newspaper.

'Oh, right. Toilet,' she says without looking up.

We have reached that stage in our working relationship where we can say a lot while using very few words.

Thursday 13th

Calis has clearly been practising ignoring me; she's in the swing of it now. I keep saying 'Hello Calis,' in a really jovial tone. I think, she imagines she's scoring one over me when she ignores me and smirks at Davina instead. I'm merely amused she's conforming to type.

This morning she comes down to the Housekeepers' Hovel and says the Cauldron Holiday Bothy needs a 'proper clean out' but more importantly, the bed linen is to be brought down for washing. I wonder if she's been eavesdropping on us because

Davina and I had just been discussing when we are going to do this. The holiday lets have finished for this season but the Holiday House hasn't been cleaned since the last lot of guests left, probably about 3 weeks previously. Not that it could be dirty. The last guests stayed for only one night and I'd cleaned it thoroughly before they arrived.

We are busy restocking the cleaning cupboard while discussing whether to go up tomorrow or the day after or next Saturday or whenever because we have to go in Davina's car as mine is too old and I'm not destroying it for any old Dowager Duchess, particularly a pretend one who has invented a mouthful of new, unpronounceable vowels.

While Calis is issuing her orders, she's standing slightly in front of me, facing Davina so while I can't see the expression on her face, I can, however, see how Davina's seems to be going through a few odd contortions. I wonder for a second or two if she's having some kind of fit.

'Tomorrow,' Calis keeps saying in her pleasant 'fingernails scratching a chalkboard' sounding voice, 'it needs to be done tomorrow.'

'Well, I've got a hospital appointment tomorrow. ' Davina is starting to look pretty stressed. 'That's why we decided maybe next week or possibly the weekend.' She's almost pleading.

'No,' Calis says firmly, 'it needs to be done tomorrow. The linen is wet and it will go mouldy.'

I don't quite manage to swallow the snort before it escapes.

She swings around to glare at me. 'Tomorrow. Understood.'

She stalks off up the ramp from the Housekeepers Hovel just as Ivo comes around the corner.

'Morning Ivo,' she says jerking her head in his direction. Ivo comes to an abrupt halt, looks horrified, panicked and terrified, in that order, before he beats a hasty retreat.

You have to admire her. She does it so effortlessly.

Davina looks very panicked now.

'What's up?' I ask. I take Calis very seriously. Oh, actually, no, I don't.

'It's you who has to go up tomorrow,' she says, 'that's what Calis was mouthing to me. Not me, you. Alone. And she told me earlier the Cauldron Holiday Bothy is your responsibility.'

'Not sure she has that much authority,' I say, 'and if she has, I need to be told by Caitlin, or Ivo or even The Dowager. And so far, no one's had that conversation with me. And besides, I've made it clear I can't go up in my car. So, hey, if you can't take us both up tomorrow, then it will have to be next week.'

'But the linen! It will go mouldy!' Poor Davina. I feel quite sorry for her.

I tell her gently the chances of the linen being wet after 3 weeks is highly unlikely, and if it is wet, how does Calis know unless she's seen it, in which case why didn't she bring it back, and really and truly, what are the chances of linen on beds being wet? How? Unless the previous occupants all pissed in their beds in which case, if they had then surely, after 3 weeks the linen will be dry by now anyway.'

Davina looks shocked. 'The bloody old bitch. Can't believe I was sucked in by that.'

Typical narcissist manipulation. They lie as easily as they breathe. I wonder how Calis is going to react if I don't go tomorrow. Oddly enough, I'm quite looking forward to it.

Friday 14th

Ivo summons me up to the office this morning. Hanging on to the rope strung along the wall, I cautiously haul myself up the nearly vertical stone steps. I'm trying to work out if there's a Health and Safety issue here.

Ivo is looking really pissed off. I'm guessing Calis has visited.

'I hear Cauldron Holiday Bothy is dirty,' he says glaring at me.

'Is it? Really? How? I've been cleaning it all summer.'

He stops for a minute and thinks about this. 'Well, Calis told me it is and there's wet linen on the beds in danger of going mouldy which needs to be brought down for washing.'

'Oh, has she been up there and seen it then?' I ask innocently. I'm waiting for the penny to drop. It takes a while. It's painful to watch.

'Well, no.' He shifts uncomfortably and won't look at me. Out of the corner of my eye, I see Caitlin smile and drop her head. Maybe she witnessed his brutal slaying at the hands of The Conservator.

'But I did ask you to go up and clean it after the last guests left,' he declares glaring aggressively at me.

No, you didn't, I think. Oh, here we go. Buck passing. I know absolutely, I've never had any conversation with Ivo about Cauldron Holiday Bothy. Cleaning it is organised between Caitlin and me. Actually, it is Caitlin who told me not to worry about rushing up to clean it after the last guests because no one else was booked in and maybe it would be good to set aside some time to give it a deep clean. Made sense to me.

'Well, I'm happy to go any time but someone will have to take me up there.' I tell him with a smile. Oh, I am so obliging.

'Are you going up to the Holiday House today?' Calis asks or she may have been snarling but I wasn't looking, after I return to the Housekeepers' Hovel. I figure it must be painful for her to actually have to speak to me. I take a minute to enjoy the situation.

Small pleasures.

'Can't. Davina's away and my car wouldn't make it.' I throw this over my shoulder as I scuttle off quickly before she has time to explode.

Monday 17th

I'm late this morning but only because the banter at the drawbridge went on for a bit longer than usual. By the time I make it down to the Hovel, Davina is looking worried.

'Calis has been told she has to go up to clean Cauldron Holiday Bothy.'

Oh good. It turns out Mrs Upstairs has issued instructions. Calis has gone up to the house with her acolyte, Morbidly Moaning Murdo. No doubt they will come back filled with tales of woe and destruction. I feel confident there will soon be some kind of retribution against me.

They return just as Davina and I are leaving.

'Oh hello,' I say in my usual 'I'm a bit thick' way. 'How was it up there?'

'Dreadful,' Calis says menacingly to Davina even though I am the one asking but she does that all the time now. 'Mice everywhere. They've eaten their way through a bed cover, a tablecloth, some of the cushions and through the leather sofa. It's complete destruction up there.'

'Oh, poor mice they must be very hungry then?' It's good she's put herself in the position of never speaking to me unless she absolutely has to because it pretty much allows me to say anything to her. Within reason. I'm sure I know where the mark is so I don't overstep it.

'And the place is filthy,' she adds for good measure. Her eyes flicker my way. She can't resist looking at me.

'Was the linen wet?' I ask innocently. She's carrying it in her arms and it's clearly not wet. Or mouldy.

'I don't know how you've got the nerve,' Davina whispers to me even though we are way out of earshot.

'Oh, I'm pretty sure there will be some kind of payback,' I say. Of this, I am very confident.

Monday 23rd

Turns out she's not really American. Her family fled from Bohemia after WWII. Not a real American and not a real Duchess. Daily Mrs Upstairs becomes less than I thought she was. While I am disappointed, I am also relieved. I know a fake when I see one and for a short while, I thought my fake-ometer was off.

I now realise after 2 weeks working at Cauldron Manor and then heading up to her summer house, this is truly domestic service. It's nothing like that little flirtation I had with it over the summer doing a bit of vacuuming, dusting and occasionally cleaning Cauldron

Holiday Bothy. This is the real deal. Not sure how to take it.

After the Manor - still just vacuuming and dusting thankfully - we go up to The House. From there it goes like this:

We sweep the kitchen floor and mop it while Manfred is out shopping, or possibly hiding in the shed drinking beer. Or both. We raid the fridge and suck down a few raspberries or grapes or any other interesting titbit. Then we head to the Library walking on our tippy-toes because The Dowager is having her breakfast in the dining room which we have to walk past, and she can't be inconvenienced or disturbed by hearing us. Yeah, I can see how that must be a struggle for her. It must be easier for her to think the cleaning is done by magic rather than people.

The Library is on the ground floor but in the other wing. Here we have to clean out the fireplace. Davina shows me how to do this by sucking all the ashes up with the vacuum cleaner. So much faster and cleaner than sweeping them into a bucket. While one of us is doing this, however, the other keeps watch in case Mrs Upstairs decides to check on us since doing it like this is a big no-no.

We make up the fire and then vacuum the room. Davina shows me where Mrs Upstairs hides petals and leaves to make sure we vacuum properly. We suck them up and anything else that looks like an obvious trap while ignoring the rest before heading across the hallway into the Drawing Room where we blow the dust off the tables; faster than using a cloth and you don't have to move one hundred and one knick-knacks and photos out of the way. I'm always nervous about touching them because I know one day, I'll break one. We empty and refill the ice bucket, refill the water jug with filtered water because heaven forbid, she might ingest a pollutant lurking in the common people's water the rest of us have to drink. We then hunt down the glass she used, this can be anywhere in the house, wash it (with non-organic non-eco-friendly dishwashing liquid. I guess it's cheaper) and replace it next to the water jug.

Then we creep out into the foyer by the back door near the dining room. This is always a dangerous moment because she can appear at any time. Today I luck out because she catches me struggling up the stairs with the vacuum cleaner and tells me off because I might damage the bannisters. I resist asking if she expects me to levitate up with the vacuum cleaner instead but to my immense surprise, she tells me to use the lift.

The lift? Really? Where? How had I not noticed it before? Probably because it's about the size of a coffin... oh now why did I choose that word? And very carefully hidden.

I finally find it by the Drawing Room door. Once inside, the vacuum cleaner perches painfully on my toes; there's nowhere else for it to go because the space is so small. When the door closes, it's dark. Very, very dark. Very, very, very dark. I stand in there waiting for the bloody thing to start moving and nothing happens except all the oxygen is getting used up and I am slowly suffocating to death. I frantically pat the walls trying to find some buttons to press while trying to keep breathing but all the oxygen had gone and I'm beginning to see stars when suddenly, without warning, it begins to move. Very slowly; very, very slowly.

By the time it reaches the next floor, I am a split second away from screaming and trying to claw my way out. I've lost all sense of perspective and actually feel as if I am lying horizontally in a coffin. It is a bit of a shock when the door opens to find I'm still very upright.

Mrs Upstairs is standing there, with her lips compressed into a very firm line, holding the lift door open.

'You have to press the start button,' she explains in patronising tones. I don't care. I am so relieved to see daylight, I sort of erupt out onto the landing and exclaim before I can stop myself.

'Jeez, it's bloody dark in there!'

She tuts and probably rolls her eyes but I am beyond caring. And anyway, I am busy hanging over the bannisters gasping for breath.

'And I meant,' she says in her fake posh voice, 'for you to put the vacuum cleaner in the lift while you used the stairs. There isn't enough room (she pronounces it 'rim') for the both of you.'

Oh well, forever branded as an idiot now.

Finally feeling calm and breathing normally, I go around the corner to find Davina convulsed in paroxysms of laughter lying on Mrs Upstairs' dressing room floor. She is still wiping tears of laughter from her eyes an hour later.

From there we run into her bedroom and one of us makes the bed (yes, seriously). We use old, pure linen sheets (the ones that wrinkle in horror as soon as you look at them) with a date inked on the corner. This corner must never be seen of course so it is tucked in at the bottom corner. (The dates range from 1949 to 1975. Really? With her money, you'd think she could afford some nice modern Egyptian cotton fitted sheets).

Once the bed is made, the top linen sheet is folded carefully over the blanket and duvet, then the corner, on the side Mrs Upstairs gets into bed, is folded back into a sort of envelope shape because heaven forbid, she has to pull them back like normal people do before getting into bed. I mean how Upstairs is that?

But that's not the end of it. Wait for this. Once her sheet/blanket/duvet envelope has been formed correctly, we then have to iron it!

Yes. Iron it.

Not lying.

And it's not just the folded over envelope bit either but all the rest of the turned over sheet as well as her pillowcases. Seriously. I kid you not. While they are actually on the bed; while the pillowcases are actually encasing the pillows. We also have to iron her duvet if it looks too crumpled. I think Davina is joking when she first tells me. I can't decide if I'm amused or outraged. I'm certainly a bit gobsmacked.

While one of us deals with this, the other takes her bedside tray downstairs to wash her glass, cup and saucer, refill her kettle and fill up her water carafe. A lemon is placed on a small wooden plate next to the cup and saucer for her early morning drink. I prefer coffee myself.

When this task is completed, we run downstairs to the dining room to clear her breakfast things while she's faffing about in her bathroom. She spends hours in her bathroom. Seriously, I've never known anyone to spend so much time messing about with their appearance and yet manage to not look any different.

Or better.

Once we've finished clearing up after her and I've taste-tested all the jam on any left-over uneaten toast and drunk a cup of her Nespresso coffee (though I tend to drink this in the kitchen where she can't see me and where, if she comes in, I can chuck it down the sink before she sees. Odd how I'm reverting back to my 18-year-old self), I vacuum the dining room floor, the foyer and the stairs (I make Davina carry the vacuum cleaner downstairs as punishment for laughing at me).

At this point, Davina is in the little cloakroom by the back door, which is the proper back door, not the servants' one we have to use, where she cleans and polishes Mrs Upstairs boots. I refuse to do this. I have standards. Making a grown woman's bed and ironing the sheets on it is more than enough for me; cleaning and polishing her boots goes way beyond the call of any duty.

Manfred is usually preparing her lunch at this time. There's a large notebook on the table where she writes down in detail what she wants to eat. For every meal. Every dish has the name of the recipe, the name of the book where the recipe is to be found along with the page number. It's only when I look through it, I think I spot a bit of a contradiction. There are plenty of vegan, vegetarian and superfood, healthy recipes, and I know she tries to use organic food (because she so is so eco-friendly and I guess this is how she appeases her conscience about all the non eco-friendly things she uses) but these dishes are usually served alongside venison or pheasant or grouse (yes, gamey) along with a specified wine. Hmmm seems to me that while Mrs Upstairs likes the idea of eating healthily, she doesn't actually like doing it.

There's always a full week's menu in the notebook. I wonder how long it takes her to decide what she's going to eat for each meal for the next week. Must pass a few hours, I guess. We can always tell when she's having guests because she notes it down so

Manfred doesn't embarrass her by not preparing enough food. It's like eating in a restaurant every day for every meal. I wonder if she ever fancies a couple of slices of toast with marmalade. I guess only if Manfred is around to prepare it for her.

Davina tells me a story about the time she, Davina, had a disagreement with Ivo, something to do with his cutting her hours without talking it through with her, so when she arrived at The House, Mrs Upstairs could see she was upset so told her to go into the kitchen and sit down while she'd make her a cup of tea. For a split second, I thought, oh okay, so she must have a bit of a heart after all but no. Davina goes on. After looking vaguely around the kitchen for several minutes, she turned to Davina and asked; 'so where is it I actually keep my tea bags?'

How the other half lives.

When we hear her come downstairs, we wait with bated breath a few minutes while she puts on her now clean and polished boots. We then wait some more to see if she pops into the kitchen to instruct us to pay yet more attention to detail, but if not, we listen for the front door to open and the sound of her boots crunching on the gravel drive. We continue waiting while carefully listening until we hear her Range Rover start and know for certain she's on her way to terrorise everyone up at the Manor.

True, sometimes she's fooled us and just gone for a walk instead. In which case we tend to continue creeping around while pretending we don't exist but when she does finally go, we do a little jig and head upstairs to her bathroom and dressing room both of which we have to clean but mostly we just lie around on the thick carpet and snort about how ridiculous it all is. We also have a view of the drive from the window so we can see if she suddenly reappears. You can never be too careful.

While we are in there, Davina shows me a catering roll of clingfilm. Mrs Upstairs has this weird belief that if she smothers her stomach with some type of incredibly expensive shrinking cream, then wraps herself in clingfilm, she will miraculously lose weight.

Sorry love, I think a diet, fewer chocolates and more exercise would probably work a bit better.

When I get home, I begin to think I'm not sure I'm cut out for this. Seriously. If Mrs Upstairs, the vowel murderer, tells me one more time how I must 'pay attention to detail,' I may give in to my newly developing socialist rage and push her down the stairs. It's all right for her. She's got the time to sit around paying attention to detail but because she's too mean to pay us past midday even if we finish later, Davina and I are always moving at a run. I'm tempted to suggest if she ups my hourly rate to the same as Davina's (yes feeling a bit aggrieved and undervalued) then my eyesight may become clearer thus allowing me to see a little more detail that I can pay attention to. However, I hold my tongue for the time being as I'm being a little circumspect because although everyone seems to take it for granted, I'm working over the winter, no one has actually had that particular conversation with me yet.

Tuesday 24th

Mrs Upstairs has a guest coming. This is good on the one hand because it puts her in a lively almost frisky mood but on the other, however, it ratchets up her level of OCD for 'paying attention to detail'. We are to make up the bed in one of the guest rooms then thoroughly clean the room, along with the bathroom, and the windows. And not just the inside of the windows. Oh, no. The outside too.

Really?

I'm not sure how to respond to this and find myself asking Davina several times if this is right. I've never been a great window cleaner myself. Isn't that why God invented actual Window Cleaners who have ladders and proper window cleaning equipment?

For two women slightly shorter than average height who are past the first flush of youth, it's no easy task. As I hang out the window, hovering precariously over a two-storey drop to the gravel driveway below while dabbing ineffectually at the bird shit just out of reach, I find myself seriously reconsidering my career options.

Of course, the windows are not clean enough.

'It's all in the detail,' Mrs Upstairs barks, strangling a few more vowels. I am beginning to feel sorry for the English language. At least it's a slight variation on her usual 'pay attention to detail'.

I explain to her that while cleaning the windows, I found a significant amount of paint flaking off right down to the bare wood leaving it exposed to the elements. She looks suitably horrified. This is not entirely true but it is a little bit. I push the point home by asking guilelessly if it's true bare untreated wood is in danger of rotting?

At this point, she sucks her large teeth and backs out of the room.

Davina high-fives me and we get back to sucking dead flies up the vacuum cleaner, eating the chocolates put out for guests, swigging some whiskey in the decanter before ironing the sheets, pillowcases and the duvet cover. On the bed.

Really, could my life get any worse?

Wednesday 25th

The guest is minor royalty. Mrs Upstairs instructs me, murdering a few more vowels on the way, on the correct way to address him. I'm seriously feeling for my great-great-great grandfather who was transported to Australia for robbing and killing an aristocrat. Yes, I know he's not real but I'm beginning to understand his motivation for committing such a heinous crime.

When the minor royal arrives, I duck out of sight. I am not doing the cap doffing stuff for anyone; minor royalty or otherwise. Unfortunately, I meet him on the landing after cleaning Mrs Upstairs bathroom. (Davina is ill today so I'm all on my own). We do one of those little dances people do when you keep trying to pass each other on the same side.

I stop, look at him, smile and say, 'Gidday. Beaut day?' Yes, I realise I'm probably being more of a New Zealander than an actual New Zealander really is.

At which point he stops, looks at me, grins broadly and says, 'sure is?' I may revise my opinion of British royalty although I'm not sure I should be won over so easily because not only I am a New Zealander, I am also Irish.

I later hear him asking Mrs Upstairs how the move back to Cauldron Manor is progressing.

'Oh dreadfully,' she says sighing dramatically, clicking her large teeth, 'it's all so terribly stressful.'

Really? Really? Well, it may be stressful but certainly not for her since she doesn't actually have to do anything. Must be nice to move around the countryside staying in your various houses when someone else has to do ALL the packing and moving.

Manfred, who is sorting out the kitchen in preparation for the move is, I notice, beginning to look slighted hectored. Or maybe drunk. Or possibly both.

Friday 27th

Today Mrs Upstairs, big teeth clicking frantically while she works her way around her unfamiliar post accent, informs us as soon as we've finished our usual duties, we must scrub the flagstones in front of the back door. There are about 50 of them. They are large flagstones and immensely grimy. The grim is probably roughly 100 years old.

'Oh, will we get paid for the extra time?' I ask in all innocence though I notice Davina who is standing behind her, slinking away. Seems a fair question to me. After all, I don't do this for the love of it. It is only a job for which I wish to be paid.

'No,' she snaps, 'you'll just have to work harder and make sure you finish your usual duties in good time instead of wasting time as no doubt you usually do.'

Duties?

This seems a bit unfair as, in addition to our usual chores, we also have to strip the guest bedroom and clean its bathroom. It's at this point, I spot the bogey hanging out her left nostril and I can't stop myself smiling. I can see she doesn't know what to make of this so backs off looking slightly concerned.

Oh, I am both an idiot and mad woman now.

Luckily, she heads off earlier than usual to terrorise the staff up at to the Manor. Even luckier, there seems to be serious rain hovering on the horizon. We rush out and throw soapy water over the flagstones, brush up to a bit of a lather with the gardener's broom and head back to the Manor just as the heavens open.

God is a socialist.

Monday 30th

Caitlin comes down to tell me it is official, I am now to work over the winter. I pretend joy though I'm having second thoughts but a job is a job is a job. Also, I am a bit surprised no one thought to ask me if I actually wanted the job. Anyway, then she says it's for 25 hours a week which (foolishly) convinces me to go with the flow. 25 hours is worth another couple of hundred pounds a month and, besides as I'm rapidly going through the meagre savings I have left after a year's travelling through Morocco, India and Asia, I'm not about to look a gift horse in the mouth. I'm sure once the move has happened, everyone and everything will settle down. I know Davina will be happy I'm working.

NOVEMBER

Tuesday 1st– Friday 4th

Mornings are hideous at the Manor now it's closed to the public, the summer staff has left and preparations are in full swing for Mrs Upstairs to move back in. Calis the Conservator is in full narcissistic mode and horribly pissed off because Davina (wisely) has chosen this time to be ill so Calis has to put up with me, and she's not nice about it either. I've decided in the interests of sanity – mine - to claim I've broken my toe. It is actually very painful but that's because I have gout. Yes. Gout. But there is no way I'm not letting on about it since gout sounds old and fat and I am neither old nor fat. Anyway, it's truly painfully so I hobble a lot. I still have to do my two hours at the Manor before heading up to The House later in the morning.

I've been practising limping, sighing and slow dusting. Calis the Conservator is doing drama queen and emoting all over the place; 'oh look at how much I have to do' and 'she will go mad if it's not done right'.

She has recruited her family to help with the move along with Morbidly Moaning Murdo. So far, I've caught them three times gossiping about me. They don't even try to be discreet. I realise the contempt in which they hold me, is serious. I cold-shoulder Miserable Murdo which he's not dealing with it very well. He does that guilty jolly talking to me but I simply give him my best bland, expressionless stare which I sense is seriously starting to unnerve him. He's beginning to look very jumpy. When he looks at me, I gaze steadily back and all the while, I imagine I'm holding an axe. I think it's paying off.

Calis the Conservator, however, is enjoying herself. She goes into huddles with her husband, Downtrodden and her two sons, Docile and Dim where they have frantic, whispered conversations before they all stop to stare at me, docile-ly and dimly, while Calis the Conservator smirks. I smile pleasantly back at them and ask if everything is okay and is there anything I can do to help. This only makes her smirk more. I really believe she thinks I'm so dim, I haven't cottoned on to what she's doing.

I notice as they morning progress how they are all really, really good at sniggering. It sounds a little like a chorus. For a minute or two, I imagine them all sitting around the dining table practising sniggering in tune. This makes me smile and when Calis catches me smiling, for a couple of seconds, she looks a little disconcerted.

I want to phone Davina to beg her to come back to work. They are like a pack of wolves who, having isolated their prey, are circling for the kill. Or rats, possibly rats is a better description for them since they have a thin, ratty look about them. Also I quite like wolves but I really hate rats.

Trouble is there's nothing I can do. I can hardly complain to anyone simply because Calis the Callous smirks at me or sniggers about me behind my back. And besides, I've worked out Ivo and Caitlin are terrified of her. No help there then.

Sunday 6th

Except Ivo does inadvertently come to my aid. He phones me today and says as Mrs Upstairs is off for a week's holiday (this is so The House can be packed up in her absence and all her belongings moved without inconveniencing her. See, so very stressful for her...) and as Calis the Conservator has had so many years' experience moving her, and since I've broken my toe (okay yes, I do feel a little twinge of guilt about that little fib but every time my mouth says broken, my mind says gout so not a real fib. Thankfully the guilty feeling passes quickly) why don't I take a week's holiday. I pretend reluctance but inside I'm singing for joy.

I ask him how Calis the Conservator feels about that. He doesn't respond for several minutes before he says, 'well it's my decision.'

Guess he hasn't run it past The Conservator then. Brave man. Or a foolish one.

Monday 7th – Sunday 13th

During my week off, I work on curing my gout. I'm not old enough to have it and I don't drink red wine or beer and I'm not overweight. I decide it's a sympathy issue. My body feels sorry for me. I also research 'Narcissists in the Workplace'.

So far, this is what I've found.

Workplace narcissists are, underneath their public façade, seething with anger and resentment. They are often consumed with envy; they will set about undermining that which they perceive to be the source of their constant frustration such as a popular or new co-worker or a skilled employee or anyone they suspect may threaten their perceived 'position' in the workplace. Narcissists crave constant attention and will go to great lengths to secure it. They are immature, constantly complain and criticise everyone but often have a particular person they perceive to be weaker than they are who they will attempt to undermine through malicious gossip.

Identifying aspects:

- They firmly believe in their own power and superior insight
- They feel entitled to special treatment
- They do not believe the normal rules of workplace etiquette apply to them
- They are poor team members

- They seldom collaborate with others without being quarrelsome or disruptive
- They are control freaks and feel the compulsive urge to micromanage and overrule others

Characteristics

- Arrogance and self-centricity; they expect special treatment and privileges
- They can be charismatic, articulate and amusing initially or if they want something from you
- They can be patronising and critical of others but unwilling or, more commonly, are unable to accept criticism of themselves
- Likely to be paranoid; they may exhibit rage-like reaction when they cannot control a situation or their behaviour has been exposed
- They can be cruel and abusive to some co-workers, often targeting one person at a time until that person quits
- They need an ongoing "narcissist supply" of people who they easily manipulate and who will do whatever they suggest – including targeting a co-worker usually by indulging in malicious gossip about them – without question
- They are often charming and act innocent in front of managers
- They are compulsive liars

Who can Work with a Narcissist?

Certain personalities mesh well with narcissistic people in the workplace. For instance, someone with a Dependent Personality Disorder, or a submissive person whose expectations are low and are willing to absorb abuse would survive with a narcissist, possibly even thrive in such an environment. But the majority of people in the workforce are likely to suffer ill-health effects, have conflicts with the narcissist, or end up being fired, reassigned or demoted. The narcissistic bully frequently gets their way: they get promoted. This is due, in part, because narcissists are excellent liars with considerable acting skills – upper management believes them and believes their abilities are too valuable to lose.

Oops, I think Calis the Conservator was the case study for this. And Morbidly Moaning Murdo is obviously the one with the Dependent Personality Disorder. I briefly consider Manfred but decide I haven't seen enough interaction between them to judge.

Oh well, knowledge is power. Or protection. My suspicions are confirmed. One consolation is the realisation that while I know she's a narcissist, she doesn't.

Monday 14th

I return to work after my week off to find Davina waiting for me. It's such a relief to see her. It's also a relief to hear Calis the Conservator has gone on holiday. This is, it seems because she's 'so terribly exhausted after doing all the move completely on her own because everyone else seemed to assume it perfectly acceptable to go on holiday and simply leave her to do it all by herself.'

This is from Mrs Upstairs who seems suspiciously and extraordinarily angry on Calis the Conservator's behalf. I wonder if she's referencing herself. After all, it is all her stuff Calis the Conservator exhausted herself moving.

I suspect The Conservator has been tittle-tattling in Mrs Upstairs ears. I wonder if I should drop Ivo in it since it was he who told me to go on holiday.

I point out Calis the Conservator's husband, two sons and Miserable Murdo were there to help her so she wasn't entirely on her own, and as they all know from long experience exactly what to do, it was probably easier for them to just get on with it rather than having to explain it all to me. Better in the long run I was away rather than getting in the way. I think this sounds pretty reasonable but as I'm saying it, but I see Davina behind her vigorously shaking her head at me. Mrs Upstairs goes an interesting shade of puce and splutters for a bit.

She also tries to stare me down for a minute or two so I look surprised and blink a lot. It's no fun trying to have a staring out competition with someone who won't play the game. And she backs off after a minute or so.

'You're game,' Davina says when Mrs Upstairs finally departs.

'Are you scared of her?' I ask.

'A bit,' Davina admits.

Not sure how I feel about that but I'm aware we are now working in a different territory. This is not the Manor of the summer.

Tuesday 15th

After breakfast, Mrs Upstairs heads off to her bathroom. A little while later, she phones down to the kitchen to tell Manfred to send me up to her bathroom. A phone in a bathroom? Why on earth?

Davina rolls her eyes at me.

Mrs Upstairs is waiting for me at the door with her hair in large oversized rollers which give her the look of those cartoon characters, you know, the ones who look like lollipops, and an old, shabby looking dressing gown.

'I want to show you what you're not doing incorrectly.' She says slowly because I am a dim-witted domestic servant and it takes me a while to catch on.

I'm not sure about the grammar of her sentence. Something didn't sound right, or correct.

Inside her bathroom, it's as hot as a sauna.

'Here,' she barks pointing with her chubby digit at the hand basin taps, 'See! Can you see?'

I'm not entirely sure what I should or shouldn't be seeing so just keep looking.

'Oh, for goodness sake. Pay attention to detail! See, see, there's still some of the brass cleaner around the edges.' Her vowels are rebelling now. They change into an entirely different accent.

I concur she is correct but I also conclude it is only visible through a super powerful magnifying glass because I still can't see anything.

'Now make sure you clean them properly today because I don't want to come in here and with my eyes ever see this again.'

For half a minute I madly wonder if she's asking me to put her eyes out. Nope, that would be called wishful thinking.

She waves me away with a hand large enough to create a breeze.

Wednesday 16th

It is nearly time to escape. We've managed to get through the morning without seeing either Mrs Upstairs or Calis. I am hiding out in the Hovel trying to decide where to go next while avoiding detection when Davina comes in looking seriously pissed off. Mrs Upstairs, strangling an innocent vowel or two with a consonant thrown in for good measure, has just told her off for vacuuming the carpet too often. Once a day is too often apparently but if we don't do it once a day, then we're told off by Calis the Conservator for not cleaning the carpets often enough.

Too many cooks.

Hmmm it's beginning to feel this is a bit of a no-win situation.

Mrs Upstairs appears just as we are about to escape and orders me into the flower room. Here she points out a cupboard full of vases, all shapes and sizes.

'These are supposed to be cleaned until they are smear free and shining. So why am I looking at smears? Well? Why, why?'

Not sure there's an answer to that except 'don't look' but I suspect that's not the answer she requires.

'Cleaning these,' she hisses, 'is one of your duties. You will not leave today until you have washed and polished every single one. And don't imagine for one moment you will be paid extra time for it either. Maybe next time you'll make sure you have completed your daily duties before leaving.'

I open my mouth to point out I've never been told this is one of my 'duties' but she backs out (not enough room for her to turn) before I have a chance to answer.

I wait till she's out sight then go into the Hovel where Davina is hiding.

'She's fecking insane,' Davina says, 'never knew we had to do that.'

I decide Mrs Upstairs is making up stuff as she goes along. I grab my bag and coat.

'You're not leaving.'

'Yep,' I tell her, 'and if she says anything, I'll say I had a doctor's appointment.' Pathetic I know but I feel very angry at her and at the way she speaks to me.

Thursday 17th

Calis the Conservator is back. Not a long holiday then. She greets me with a big smile and a friendly hello. All my senses are immediately on high alert. Later that morning when Davina and I are in Mrs Upstairs' office/bunker checking our email using her Wifi, I ask her if she noticed the jolly tones of The Conservator.

'Yes,' she says, 'and now I think about it, it's a bit odd. Maybe it's to do with the vases you didn't clean.'

Maybe but I suspect this is something to do with the payback I'm surely overdue for my getting her sent up to clean the Cauldron Holiday Bothy. Oh, and as for the dread plague of mice she bleated on about so dramatically. Morbidly Miserable Murdo inadvertently revealed the so-called plague was nowhere near as bad as she made out. Oh, now there's a surprise.

'You need to be careful,' Davina warns me. 'I've seen what she can do.'

'Rochelle?' I ask.

'Yes. And Elissa.'

Oh wait, this is a new name.

Elissa was Head Housekeeper before Rochelle. The Conservator bullied her out of her job too. I ask Davina how she could be friends with that woman. Did she not think her behaviour was a bit unacceptable? I sense Davina feels bad about it.

'She always made it sound as if it was their fault.' She admits as we eat our way through few of Mrs Upstairs Chocolate Ginger Bites.

So far there's been no fallout re: the smeared vases. I wonder if Mrs Upstairs has forgotten but I suspect it's probably because she has more pressing things on her mind. This is slightly worrying.

Friday 18th

I have discovered after clearing out the fireplace in the Short Drawing Room, how it is not a good idea to make the fire up again immediately. The bricks are hot; hot enough it transpires for the paper to burst into flames and get the fire going. Once it happens there's not a lot I can do about it except keep feeding the fire since I don't have time to let it die down, wait for the bricks to cool down (this was the mistake I make in the first place) and make up another one before I leave work.

Mrs Upstairs is livid. It's not a colour that suits her. I can't decide if she dislikes me or not, or whether I am so immaterial to her, she barely notices my existence. In which case, it must be frustrating for her when I keep reminding her of my existence. I suspect a good servant is a discreet one.

The Conservator is so overjoyed at my fire transgression, she can barely contain herself. I've never seen her looking so joyful. I'm still waiting for the payback. She's being, well I won't go so far as to say nice, but suspiciously pleasant. And she wanders around with a kind of expectant air. I don't think it will be long now.

Saturday 19th

I text Davina to suggest we both take Monday off. We play around with the idea for a while but conclude it would be pointless. And we have one thing going for us; we know something is about to happen but The Conservator doesn't know we know. We can at least be prepared.

Oh dear, who am I turning into?

Monday 21st

Isn't long in coming. I have barely crunched through Mrs Upstairs leftover toast spread with her expensive organic butter and Manfred's homemade raspberry jam before we are summoned to the Short Drawing Room.

Mrs Upstairs starts her rant with the unacceptable wrinkles in the rugs. She makes us get down on our hands and knees to straighten them out. We must do this gently because the rugs are old, made of silk and therefore, priceless. And grubby. My hand is very dirty after a minute or two. I briefly think about the centuries of people who'd trampled all over them. I try not to think about dog shit, or horse shit or indeed sheep shit as there is a large flock of them in the next field.

I stand up at this point and clock from the expression on Mrs Upstairs face, how she is building herself up into a fine sense of rage and outrage. Seems the rugs are just a distraction to disarm us while she builds herself up to rant about the real reason she's called us up here.

'Snooping,' she says in a deadly tone although the effect is ruined a little by the teeth clicking noises accompanying the tone. She looks down at Davina who is still crouching down patting the priceless but dirty rug. 'I don't mean you, Davina,' she says, 'you've been told this many times and I know you know not to do it. But you,' she glares balefully at me. I smile back inanely which throws her for a second or two, 'opening drawers and cupboards and going through my private things, my private possessions. Well, that's cause for instant dismissal. Instant!' She's shaking with rage and stabbing the air between us with her chubby finger.

Ah, so this is the Conservator's revenge. She must have been feeling pretty confident of the end result to have made up something so pathetic.

'Well, of course,' I say smiling pleasantly while nodding in agreement, as if she's being perfectly reasonable and not a mad old bitch, 'and if I ever was snoop or look through your private things, then I would expect nothing less. Instant dismissal would absolutely be the only way to deal with such a terrible transgression. I would do the same myself.' I say this very slowly, patiently and in a tone of complete agreement with a slow nod to emphasise we are so on the same page here. I hope I'm not overdoing it but it seems to work.

Out of the corner of my eye, I see Davina, still kneeling on the floor, mouthing a silent 'fecking hell'.

Mrs Upstairs blinks madly for a few minutes, opens and shuts her mouth a couple of times then beats a hasty retreat. We wait until we hear the outside door downstairs open and slam shut before Davina high-fives me before we head for the Chinese cabinet and Mrs Upstairs' chocolate stash.

'Does this count as snooping?' Davina asks with her mouth full of liqueur truffles.

Tuesday 22nd

This morning, Davina tells me she received several texts from Calis (I guess she likes Davina since she has given her mobile phone number) asking what Mrs Upstairs wanted with me. Now, how does she know I'd been summoned? More to the point, why does she not realise it was both of us?

'Me?' I query.

'Uh huh. Odd that. I texted back and told her how I'd got into shed loads of trouble because while I was accused of snooping, the Dowager didn't say anything to you because you are new and wouldn't have known so it's all my fault because I'm responsible for making sure you do know these things.'

Oh, I really like Davina. Clever. Very clever. And Calis the Conservator did not reply.

'I sent her another text to say I nearly lost my job.'

Oh, I really, really like Davina.

Not the result Calis the Conservator was expecting I'm sure.

'We must be careful,' I say, 'and not underestimate her.'

Davina agrees. I think she's beginning to realise how toxic Calis the Conservator is.

Wednesday 23rd

I arrive this morning to find Davina nowhere in sight. This is not a good sign. I track her down to Mrs Upstairs exercise room (I say exercise room but it's really more a room full of exercise equipment and books about exercises. I think Mrs Upstairs is one of those who believes exercise is done by a kind of osmosis; you own the equipment and read all the books and this fact alone will enable you to become fit and slim without actually doing any of the said exercising), where she's pretending to vacuum up the soot that's fallen from the chimney while in reality she's simply lying on some cushions eating her way through a box of Mrs Upstairs chocolate stash.

'Not good?'

'Nope,' she shakes her head. It's difficult for her to speak with so much chocolate in her mouth. I wait for her to swallow some. 'She's snorting rockets.'

Ouch. Though this gives me a moment's pleasure as I imagine Mrs Upstairs trying to snort a rocket up her nose like cocaine but I know what Davina means. She's in a mean mood.

'I knew as soon as she opened her bathroom door and started screeching for me. I think I've seriously hurt my arm running away from her so fast carrying this bloody cleaning machine up those bloody stairs and along the bloody passage.'

Oh, lots of 'bloodys'. She is seriously pissed off.

I leave her to her misery to return cautiously to the Housekeepers' Hovel. I need some cleaning supplies and dusters for camouflage. That way I can look as if I'm busy. Sadly, I am not fast enough. Mrs Upstairs must have heard something because she's now moving down the stairs with all the grace of a baby elephant and the zeal of a newly converted missionary.

'You!' she screeches, 'who put the towels in my bathroom?'

'What's wrong?' I ask. It was Davina but I'm not about to get into the blame game.

'This towel is a MEDIUM sized one. I need a LARGE one.' She shrieks, pink in the face with the sheer effrontery at being given the wrong sized towel. She waves said offending towel in my face. I conclude either I'm still asleep and this is a disturbing dream or I've slipped into an alarming alternative reality. But to be fair she is right; a medium sized towel is much too small for her. Even a large one struggles to be large enough.

'Would you like me to get you the correct size?' I ask very calmly. (She so seriously needs to get a life. No really, I mean it. A life).

She seems affronted I even ask her this.

I take my time. I figure her bath will be getting pretty cold by now so she'll have to run another one so with luck, she'll be out of our way for another 30 minutes or so and then it will be time for breakfast. If we work it right, we may get to avoid her for the rest of the day. On the way back, I visit Davina in the exercise room and help myself to a chocolate.

When I return with the towel (the linen closet is in another wing. Bad planning although it is central to the rest of the Manor guest bathrooms except Mrs Upstairs's, of course, so she has to have her bathroom and bedroom in a really inconvenient and out of the way part of the Manor. Though true my return does take longer than it should due to the chocolate stop and my slow saunter back), she's impatiently waiting by the door of her very tacky decorated bathroom.

'What took you so long?' she demands angrily, holding out her hands for the towel.

'I'm sorry,' I say handing it over (the oldest and thinnest one I could find), 'I was just finishing my prayer for all those Syrians who are freezing to death in refugee camps in Greece.' I am moving rapidly away while saying this so the last part I throw over my shoulder as I head down the stairs.

I admit I am only a little bit brave.

Thursday 24th

We learn today that tomorrow afternoon, Mrs Upstairs is going away for a week. She's on holiday which means we're on holiday. Not really, we still have all our work and then some but I mean on holiday from her. There are also guests due, 14 of them, the day after she returns so we must prepare all the guest rooms. This means giving them a good topping and bottoming. Not a term I'm familiar with but I get the picture. Turns out no one's cleaned the rooms since the previous winter. Oh, joy. This means there will be window cleaning involved.

At least today it is The Conservator getting it in the neck. She must get Mrs Upstairs' clothes ready before packing them into the correct cases. This is immensely stressful for Mrs Upstairs. I get it. Making sure your servants are doing everything properly and in the specific way you require, is hard work even when you're sitting on a chair in your dressing room drinking copious amounts of Harrods organic tea (Not. Actually, Tetley's from the staff cupboard in the kitchen) made with filtered water (Not. Actually, tap water from the bathroom). Davina, Manfred and I are in the kitchen, however, drinking Harrods organic tea made with filtered water. We can't taste the difference so I doubt she can.

Morbidly Moaning Murdo is hyperventilating because he has to drive her to the airport in her Range Rover (see so eco-aware). This, she insists, he also clean from top to bottom but somehow, he never manages to do it well enough for her exacting (I say exacting but I mean neurotic) standards. I try to explain to him there's no point busting a gut trying to get it right because he'll never manage to no matter how hard he tries. He may as well just clean it as much as he can be bothered because either way, he'll get a rollicking. I can see he's kind of won over until The Conservator comes into the kitchen and instructs him to make sure he cleans the Range Rover as well as he can because 'she'll go mad' otherwise.

I've noticed The Conservator is keeping her distance since 'snoopgate' but I'm not stupid enough to think that's the end of it. I'm pretty sure she's plotting.

She keeps going off into whispering huddles with Morbid Murdo and looking pinch-lipped at me if I ever dare hove into view. I keep up my friendly idiot facade. At least I know she's plotting something but she doesn't know I know. Oh, am I beginning to sound paranoid? What is this place doing to me?

When we finally finish our shift and walk to the carpark, I point out to Davina how I'm surprised Mrs Upstairs' Range Rover is at least 3 years old. It turns out she used to get a new one every year because the then manager of the local Land Rover dealership gave her a free one but there's a new manager now and he doesn't see why she can't pay for a new one.

Good for him. What's with giving a new Range Rover to someone who can afford to buy it? Seems odd to me.

Friday 25th

I suspect Mrs Upstairs took my reference to Syrian refugees to heart. Not in a nice way, unfortunately.

'Syrians are Muslims (she pronounces it 'muzlins'),' she says coldly when I misjudge the time and walk into the kitchen while she is still lurking by the refrigerator guzzling a large glass of coconut and pomegranate juice (it's so loaded with sugar, it leaves a coating on your teeth. I know, I've tasted it. Not one for my shopping list).

Not sure how this is significant but clearly, she thinks her statement is noteworthy.

'No kidding,' I say.

She purses her lips at my comment. Perhaps 'kidding' is too common. Or too familiar.

'Yes, Muzlins. Not refugees.'

Does one automatically cancel out the other? Don't know how to respond to that.

Monday 28th

Today, upstairs, the Manor is freezing. It's so cold, it's not funny. Mrs Upstairs had all the heating turned off because she's away and she doesn't want to waste heat. I am shocked. Truly. We still have to work in there. This is the 21st Century. Someone needs to tell her.

We head up to the guest rooms to try to find one with a heater. We figure we'll clean that one first. Unfortunately, the room we find is so big and the heater so small it makes not one single iota of difference. We drag it off to a smaller bedroom. The heat might penetrate some of the cold in a small space. No such luck. It merely warms the air in a two inch radius, the rest of the room stays Arctic. We decide to forego the cleaning full stop.

I head down to her office/bunker to use the Wi-Fi so I can check the government website for the legal minimum temperature for working in. Turns out there's

no such thing but there is, however, a guideline of 16°
or 13° if you're doing physical work. Either way, when
we retrieve the barometer from the wine cellar and take
it upstairs, the temperature hovers around 3°. Too cold
to work. I'm seriously pissed off. I cannot believe her
selfishness.

We decide instead to put on our coats and go
around all the rooms and bathrooms to get an idea of
what we will have to do while checking to make sure
all the taps, lights, handles etc work properly. It's our
nod to 'paying attention to detail'. We compile a small
list then move back downstairs onto the first floor. This
is still damn cold but not as bad as the rooms upstairs.

Davina decides to clean the ancient artefacts on
the landing while I go in to check on Mrs Upstairs
tacky bathroom. I say tacky but I mean vulgar. I'm sure
it was once a beautiful room. It has a lovely arched
ceiling but she's put in one of those makeup mirrors,
you know, the ones actors have in their dressing rooms
with bulbs all around the sides. I guess all the better to
see yourself. Must be an egotist's idea of heaven. The
drawers and cupboards are full of makeup, creams and
potions. Really, more than enough for a small shop. If
she sat in there all day putting it all on and taking it off
again, I doubt she'd ever get through more than a 1/100
of it.

Here I discover that while she's turned her heated
towel rail off, it's an easy job to turn it back on. Then I
hear Davina shouting down to Morbidly Miserable

Murdo who is lurking miserably in the vestibule, about all the things we found needing to be replaced or repaired. I don't hear what he says but Davina calls through to me to check what they were. I start to answer but decide it's ridiculous for me to tell her so she can tell him, I may as well tell him myself. I go out and start walking down the stairs just as I hear him shout, 'Oh for feck's sake you stupid woman, do you seriously think I can hear through several feet of thick concrete.' Then he mutters, 'stupid woman.'

'No,' I say coldly coming down the stairs but just out of his sight and then I hear her, The Conservator muttering and sniggering. Should have known she'd have something to do with it. When she's not around he's just morbidly miserable but when she is, he's morbidly miserable and mean, 'that's why I'm coming downstairs to tell you.' But I stop where I am just around the corner and still out of sight. I rattle off the list and go back up to Mrs Upstairs bathroom. Davina sees the look on my face and scuttles in behind me.

'Fecking rude bastard,' she says, 'hell it's hot in here. How did you manage that?'

I don't say anything because I figure The Conservator may be lurking and I suspect she's good at making mountains out of molehills.

Then I decide. 'I'm going to say something to him.'

Davina immediately looks panicked. She hates conflict. I feel sorry for her. This is not the right place to be working if you hate conflict. Then I remember I don't either. Better to say something when I'm not so angry.

I decide I'm giving myself the rest of the day off. It's too cold to work. I drag Davina upstairs to the office, which is a bit of a feat since we both hang on to the rope handrail and to each other while trying really hard not to fall backwards down the stone steps to the flagstones below. Hit those from a height and you'd definitely be past your 'best by' date.

We tell them (strength in numbers) it's too cold to work, it's way below the government guidelines (always handy to throw in what sounds like a bit of legislation) and insist it needs to be sorted before we can get the bedrooms ready for the influx of guests (which is exactly the bit of blackmail it sounds).

Everyone in the office gives us that silent but terrified 'rabbit caught in headlights' stare because it means someone will have to contact Mrs Upstairs to inform her of this. I sense their panic. It's nice when she's away because then everyone can relax and pretend they work for a normal person. We leave them to it. I sense there will be a bit of buck-passing going on before someone, probably Caitlin, will be bullied into it.

Tuesday 29th

Morbidly Miserable Mean Murdo passes me on the walk up to the Manor.

'Good morning,' he says cautiously.

I ignore him. I have my pride. Besides I've worked out he's only mean when The Conservator is around. I've also worked out she too is much worse when she's got her cohort Grumpy around her. Alone, she's a bit more amenable which doesn't mean nicer or even a better person. It means she's a bit careful when she's on her own. Still, Miserable Murdo should grow some balls. I've been nice to him, so I didn't deserve his rudeness.

Inside the Manor, thankfully, it's marginally warmer so I guess someone made the call. Mrs Upstairs bathroom, however, is really warm since neither of us bothered to turn her towel rail off. We hang out in there for a while drinking her posh coffee and trying out some of her potions. Only the ones on display on top of the table though because we wouldn't want anyone to accuse us of snooping.

Later, as I clean the black mould from the windows in one of the large and still cold guest bedrooms, I make a comment about how I wonder if this is really the right place for me. I'm sensing this is not the stress-free and calm job I was looking for. Davina, however, gets a panicked look on her face.

'You'll be fine,' she says, 'you're going nowhere. And besides, she goes away a lot during the winter. And when she's here, she has friends... I mean people, staying.'

But I realise that is more about her than me. I decide to say nothing more but I'm thinking this is no longer any fun.

As I'm leaving, Caitlin calls me to wait. Apparently, Mrs Upstairs instructed her to inform me I am to work the same hours as Davina while she's away. This means 3.5 hours instead of 5. Not sure how I feel about it but I guess I can stand it for a week. And besides, it's cold and lonely without Davina for that extra 1.5 hours.

DECEMBER

Friday 2nd

Mrs Upstairs isn't arriving back till after 11 which means by the time Morbidly Moaning Murdo returns with her we will have left. Bonus.

We spend the morning going through all the guest rooms and guest bathrooms making sure everything is just so, though no doubt Mrs Upstairs will find something amiss. You can always find something if you look hard enough.

The last thing I do is put out chocolates on little dishes beside each of the guests' beds. I suddenly run out of chocolates with two rooms still to go. I suspect this is because Davina and I have been dipping into the boxes randomly and gluttonously over the past week. I've put 5 chocolates in each dish so I figure if I go back and take one off each, I should have enough for all the rooms. However! I discover there are not 5 chocolates in each dish but 4. I eventually find Davina picking aphids of Mrs Upstairs potted lilies while looking suspiciously like a squirrel only with chocolates stored in her cheeks instead of nuts.

'I couldn't help myself,' she slurps. We head back to the Chinese cabinet in the Short Drawing Room just to check if there are more boxes stashed somewhere. I mean, don't Chinese cabinets have secret drawers or something. Luckily, we find boxes and boxes and boxes! It's extraordinary. I can see why Mrs Upstairs doesn't lose weight, what with only imagining doing exercise and eating her body weight in chocolates... no chance.

Saturday 3rd

Oh hell. It's -4° this morning. It may be Saturday but I have to be at the Manor because of Mrs Upstairs guests, 14 of them, and we must behave in a domestic servant type manner.

They arrive just as we finish putting the water carafes in their rooms. We are supposed to use filtered water from the kitchen but because we're allowed to carry only one carafe (they're crystal and expensive, and as we are of the lower orders, we are, therefore, clumsy and may drop them) and this means going back and forth 14 times up and down several flights of stairs, so we use water from their bathrooms instead. Davina tells me two of the guests are Mrs Upstairs' oldest friends but the rest are their children and their friends who are all aged between 18 and 25. I suggest to Davina, if that's the case, surely wine or beer would be better.

'Don't worry,' she says gloomily, 'there will be more than that in their rooms by the end of the weekend.'

This sounds ominous.

They arrive and I see they are indeed mostly young and very posh and have clearly perfected the technique of looking at you while managing not to see you. Still, their youthful exuberance has made Mrs Upstairs positively skittish. However, along with our usual chores of cleaning the Short Drawing Room and making up the fire, we also have to clean and make up the big fire in the Long Drawing Room

The fireplace here takes up one wall at the end of a long narrow room. It is seriously big enough to house a refugee family (but not a Muzlin one... just saying).

It has to be made up so: scrunched up sheets of the Financial Times (would she notice, say the Daily Record? Does the Financial Times give a better class of fire?) with between 18 and 20 pieces of kindling, depending on size, placed on top which is followed by an upright ring of 5 short sticks (logs) which are cut to precisely 12 inches. Surrounding that is another ring of 8 medium sticks which are cut to 18 inches and lastly, these are then surrounded by another ring of 12 large sticks cut to 24 inches. And Mrs Upstairs counts them. I kid you not. I am relieved she doesn't get out a tape measure and check the length.

All her fires must be made up to these kinds of precise numbers and measurements. There are cupboards throughout the Manor full of logs (sorry, sticks) cut to these specific lengths. I don't bother to replenish the baskets beside the fires because, after all, I'm not sure which cupboards are which and I wouldn't want to be caught looking in a cupboard I shouldn't be looking in. You never know when 'snoopgate' may come back and bite you on the bum.

Manfred is stressing in the kitchen. Fenella has come to help him prepare for the residing guests and a few others who seem to have wandered in for breakfast. I'm not sure if they've been invited or not but it's not up to me to say anything. The breakfast is enormous which is good for several reasons; it will take them ages to get through it all so they should finish about the time we are leaving, we have plenty of time to make beds and clean bathrooms, and, hopefully, there will be loads left over; so, lunch for us. Result.

Yep, they finish breakfast by lunchtime. Davina and I quickly go in and munch our way through most of the leftovers then stuff whatever we can't eat into our bags. Well, there have to be some perks to have such a menial and largely thankless job and besides, it all gets thrown out anyway. Seriously. For someone who is supposedly into conservation, recycling and eco-friendly stuff, it all seems a bit selective and based on that which doesn't inconvenience her. Anyway, at this rate, I may not have to buy food for a couple of days. Always after a saving.

Through the closed Dining Room door, I hear Mrs Upstairs slaughtering a couple of consonants while bullying her guests into putting on their boots to go for a brisk walk. She's not going, of course. Heaven forbid she ever does anything more strenuous than shouting at us or running a bath. She heads to her sitting room/office/bunker to hunker down by the fire with her morning tea and homemade shortbread until lunch time which will be in about ½ an hour by my reckoning.

Apart from the parents, who eccentrically wear shorts and sandals despite the freezing temperatures and wave us away with a practised flick of the wrist, there are also a couple of older guests who don't go out for a walk but retire instead to the drawing room. One is a cool and funky (not) American hippy who hasn't worked out that long grey hair pulled back in a ponytail only works if you have hair all over your head and not a few thin strands around the sides. I should be kinder because he did at least talk to us, unfortunately, he was so intent on being cool and 'spiritual', my attention kept wandering. The way he proselytised, you'd think he'd discovered yoga and meditation all by himself. We let ourselves be patronised for a few minutes before edging backwards away from him, nodding politely as we made our exit mid-lecture. After all, we are not paid to listen to her guests and nor are we paid if we go over our allotted time.

You have to draw the line somewhere.

I forgot to mention something weird that happened earlier in the morning when I went up to Mrs Upstairs' bedroom, which I do with resentment as I still can't get my head around a grown woman expecting someone to make her bed every day, when I caught Calis (I'm sure she must sleep in the place because she always seems to be lurking) carefully examining the bottom sheet on the bed. Initially, I thought she was probably checking my bed making skills but her reaction when I walked in on her was a bit extreme and unlike her. She actually looked embarrassed and quickly drew the covers up while barking at me to make sure I dusted the window ledges.

When I asked her what she was doing (though why I asked, I'm not sure), she got all huffy, told me to mind my own business and instructed me to make the bed properly.

I mention this to Davina as we are leaving at which point, she rolls her eyes and pretends to vomit.

I try really hard to resist asking what but I can't help myself.

'That's Calis checking to see if Mrs Upstairs had sex with that old hippy,' Davina throws over her shoulder at me as she's getting into her car. She shuts the door, waves and drives off.

With difficulty, I resist the urge to throw myself at her car and demand she explain further.

I try very hard to not to think about it. Any of it. Either Mrs Upstairs having sex full stop or Calis looking for evidence. My mind can't handle that much boggling.

Sunday 4th

As Davina isn't feeling well today, to take the pressure off her, I reluctantly agree to polish Mrs Upstairs' expensive Ugg boots. I do this after I've cleaned all the bathrooms, made up all the beds and removed all the used condoms and empty alcohol bottles from the guest rooms. They partied until 4 am apparently. And clearly, judging by the mess, they know how to party. Mrs Upstairs is looking a little wan which is an improvement on her usual livid look.

I try really hard to not think about her, possibly, having a wild old night with Mr Hippy. But to be honest, it's made me look at him in a new light. I'm a bit nicer to him this morning as I suspect he could be off his head. I mean. Him. Her. Sex. Together. Those two. No, seriously. Not going there.

As I stand looking out through the barred window in the old servants' quarter, polishing Mrs Upstairs' boots after I finish making her bed, I think to myself; if anyone this time last year had told me I would be employed to make the bed and polish the boots of perfectly capable, middle-aged woman, I will have thought them mad.

When I return to the main part of the Manor, Mrs Upstairs is waiting for me, mouth pursed unattractively, big hair billowing. She snatches her boots off me, scans them intently for a minute or two before pointing out a few minor transgressions re-mud removal. She has taken to speaking to me in icy tones and very slowly as if I'm a bit dim-witted. Not sure whether I should be relieved or insulted.

Tuesday 6th

Davina is ill again. Though it could be a reaction to the previous day's mad cleaning up after the guests. Stripping 14 beds and gathering 100s of towels is no mean feat especially when we still had to clean up after Mrs Upstairs, and she wouldn't give us any extra time. I wonder if we had gone over our allocated hours of work, would she have paid us? I doubt it. Consequently, we worked at a run.

Mrs Upstairs now speaks to me as little as possible now except to repeat things. Or shout. She shouts at me this morning because I'd put the wrong sized lemon on the tray next to her bed. The one I put on it is too small and not perfect enough. (Seriously. Clearly, lemons have a class system). As she lets rip and tortures a few more English vowels, I hear the hint of a southern drawl. Oh well, I guess you can take the girl out of the south but you can't take the south out of the girl. While I am thinking this, I didn't notice she'd stopped her rant. I go back into the 19th century to find her glaring at me.

'Okay,' I say. Not sure what else to say.

'Oh, you are so stupid,' she snaps at me (hmm. Pot? Kettle?) before creaking away. Seriously, creaking. I think it's her corsets. She walks in a stiff, well-padded way but I also know this is true because every Monday I take her laundry down to The Conservator's lair to be washed.

'I have a PhD,' I mutter to her retreating back. I didn't expect her to hear me but maybe she's not as old or deaf as she looks or maybe my voice is louder than I realise. She stops, turns and glares at me. She blinks several times while her mouth does some gymnastics before she pulls her shoulders back – all the better for glaring down her nose at me.

'And I have a title,' she announces imperiously before turning and creakily sweeping off again.

I am a bit stunned.

For my last 1.5 hours, Calis the Conservator has me running up and down more flights of stairs than I care to remember. It's frustrating because as soon as I return with whatever she sent me up for, she suddenly remembers something else so I have to go all the way back. In the end, I decide to take my time and besides I've found more chocolates and the alcohol the guests must have brought up to their bedrooms from the drinks cupboard in the Long Drawing Room. I sit in the furthest bathroom from where I can hear her approaching if she decides to come looking for me, and where I spend the last half hour of my shift, reading old Punch magazines, gobbling chocolates and swigging leftover whiskey. I sneak out at the end of my shift hoping I haven't drunk so much I'm over the limit for driving.

I notice my jeans are getting awfully tight.

Wednesday 7th

I left a tube of the brass cleaner in Mrs Upstairs' bathroom. She comes stomping and wobbling down the stairs and presents it to me as if it is a trophy of some sort.

'This is ridiculous,' she says breathing fire. 'Is it too much to ask for you to pay attention to detail? (Oh shit, fed up hearing that one). Is it too much to ask for you to remove all the cleaning products from my personal space? Is it? Is it?' She's seriously screeching now and has gone an alarming (yet interesting) colour. It clashes with her complexion which is I suspect 2/3 Prairie Face Care and 1/3 snake oil. Whatever it is, it's not a combination that's doing much to improve her looks. I wonder if all the Turmeric drops she sucks down every morning are contributing to the faint yellow hue on her face. Or perhaps she's just liverish.

I shake my head and say nothing because I think she is in danger of bursting a gasket.

I try to put myself in her position in the hope it may help me be a better servant. Nope. I guess I'm just not that batshit crazy. Or egotistical.

Thursday 8th

This morning, Mrs Upstairs calls me upstairs before I've had time to take off my coat. She doesn't speak but breathes volumes.

Into the bathroom we go. I'm convinced she only spots so much wrong in her bathroom because she spends most of her day in there.

She points to the shower attachment connected to the bath taps. 'This,' she says in her pained barely controlled anger voice, 'was turned to 'shower'. She repeats this several times because I must have my dim-witted servant expression on and she thinks it's real.

'okay,' I say carefully. I don't want to rile her too much. She's got that trapped rattlesnake look about her.

'It has leaked and soaked all the wood. Soaked all the WOOD.' She's moving fast into hysteria and her teeth are clacking furiously. Then she takes a breath and calms down. 'You have caused serious and unnecessary damage to this.' She says very slowly.

Oh ho, interesting the automatic assumption I'm responsible. I know I not. Mainly because I didn't clean her bath the previous day. I ran out of time so Calis had to do some work for a change.

I wait until I see she's worked herself up into a state of barely controlled indignation before I suggest she's better off mentioning it Calis. At first, she doesn't seem to hear me and then she does rapid blinking (I guess that's the way she changes her brain gear, I can almost hear the cogs clicking). She glares at me and asks why in a very pained and clipped voice. Either that or she is murdering more vowels.

'Because Calis cleaned your bathroom yesterday.' I tell her. Blow this not playing the blame game. I'm not taking the can for Calis. I've come to the conclusion, it's every woman for herself in this place.

Calis, however, has come in behind me and hears what I said.

'No, I didn't,' she says. See breathes/ lies. Same thing to her.

Mrs Upstairs looks pained. I get it. It must be difficult to have servants who answer you back and even worse to discover they are then possibly lying while doing it.

I now make a point of photographing said tap in the correct position when later I finish cleaning her bathroom. This I resolve to do every day. You can't be too careful in this place I realise.

Friday 9th

Davina is here today. She doesn't look well but while I'm worried about her health, I'm selfishly grateful she's around. Especially as today I see a really extreme side to Mrs Upstairs. I'm wondering about her mental health.

She surprises us before we can escape. She shouts from the flower room, a dungeon-like cell situated under the stone stairs and hidden behind a heavy studded door. Through the door, her voice is muffled until Davina opens it, and the decibels are about as high as those of a fire engine siren. For a minute I think she's injured herself... but no.

'It's broken,' she's shrieking and shaking (I mean really shaking) with rage. She points to a vase lying shattered into a million pieces on the floor. 'Pick that up and put it back together again.' (seriously?)

Davina timorously points out it's after 12 and technically she's now off the clock.

For a minute, Mrs Upstairs just stares wild-eyed at her and then says (surprisingly), 'all right dear, you can go. But you...' she turns back to me and fixes her gimlet beady eyes on me, 'will fix it before you leave. And I hope it will teach you to be more careful with my things.'

I cannot believe I just heard that. I didn't break the damn thing after all. I am so shocked, I'm speechless.

'Feck me,' Davina says under her breath as Mrs Upstairs sweeps out with all the grace of an overloaded cargo ship limping into port.

We stand and stare at each other. I have no idea what to say to this.

'Hang on,' says Davina, 'I know where there's another one like this. I'll just get it and leave it here.'

Nice plan but I suspect Mrs Upstairs might notice there're no broken bits.

'Leave it,' I say, 'let's just sweep the bits up and chuck them out. If she says anything, we can tell her she told us to.' I figure she thinks I'm pretty dim-witted so I may as well play on it.

Saturday 10th

I was told last night I must come into the Manor today because with Davina being away in the week so many things weren't done properly. Caitlin is keen to assure me that yes, I will be paid but sorry, not overtime. She begs me for a while because I am really reluctant. I need my days off to recover. Seriously, all the time-travelling I do back to the 19th century is taking its toll on my health. I give in because I feel sorry for her.

When I arrive, Mrs Upstairs is buttering up the gardener who has to bring all the logs in for her fire. I wasn't fast enough. Usually I can avoid her first thing. She purses her lips at me but doesn't mention the vase. Maybe she had time to re-think her actions and realise she could be insane. Or she's forgotten all about it.

Note to self: check her memory. Seems to me it comes and goes a bit. Is she old enough for Alzheimers?

It's lonely without Davina and today, as I sit perched on the edge of Mrs Upstairs' antique porcelain bathtub circa 1901, polishing its brass and copper fittings, it occurs to me I hate brass, copper and baths. So last century. What's wrong with a nice tiled shower with steel fittings? True, these ancient things are lovely to have if you're not the one who has to clean them.

It takes me at least an hour every day to get them shiny enough to satisfy Mrs Upstairs' rapidly expanding exacting, and now borderline hysterical, standards and then another 10 minutes or so to clean off the black residue the brass cleaner leaves on the porcelain. Of course, I am not allowed to use any cleaning products or abrasives on the porcelain because I can destroy it. This instruction is now repeated every day because, as a domestic servant, I obviously have a very small brain and cannot, therefore, retain this crucial information. Luckily, I have discovered the magical cleaning quality of Mrs Upstairs expensive herbal toothpaste.

I am very careful to make sure I take the brass cleaner away with me.

Sunday 11th

My only day off this week. Minus 3° this morning. What idiot gave temperatures a number. I see -3 and I think bloody hell it's freezing. Otherwise, I'd just register it's a bit cold and not think more about it. Now I'm obsessed with the number. When it gets to 0, I may get up if I can face the sub-0 temperatures in the bathroom of the house I'm housesitting. See. Obsessed by numbers. Thank God, I don't have to get up to go to work today. This whole Domestic Service lark is, frankly, no longer a lark. I begin to see it as a Comedy of Errors or possibly, Trial by Torture.

Monday 13th

Minus 6° this morning! Not sure what it means except really very cold. At least Mrs Upstairs likes her warmth, apart from in her bedroom where she keeps the window open with no heating on but because she sleeps curtained off by heavy velvet drapes in her four-poster bed, it gets warm in there. Of course, she has a top of the range electric blanket. It's so cold in her room today I can see my breath and my hands go an interesting shade of blue. Luckily, the iron I use on her sheets and pillowcases sends out a little squeak of heat. I'm supposed to iron her bottom sheet as well, but I just do the bit you can see when the duvet is pulled back.

I still can't believe I'm doing it while I'm doing it. I mean what's so bad about a few creases in your sheets? Maybe she thinks if she lies on creased sheets, they'll cause her skin to wrinkle. Who knows? She's a migrant and pretending to be an aristocrat. Perhaps there's a female English unmarried aristocrat somewhere feeling aggrieved because some damned migrant stole her job.

It's always a relief to spend time in her bathroom after making her bed even if it is to polish brass and copper fittings and clean her toilet with salt and vinegar because in there, the bathroom I mean not the toilet, the temperature is tropical. If I had the time, I could do a run between bathroom and bedroom and bathroom and bedroom like the Swedes do with a sauna and snow. Unfortunately, there is a corridor of about half a mile between them so the effect will probably be wasted.

Davina is not coming back to work for a week. The Conservator tells me this while smirking. Maybe it's a kind of tic? I already know this but don't let on. Davina and I have decided it's better to pretend we hardly know each other. For some reason, this feels like a sensible thing to do because I sense Calis is jealous of Davina's friendship with me. Before I arrived, Calis had Davina all to herself to manipulate her at her will and The Conservator strikes me as a jealous kind of person. No doubt it's part of her Narcissist Personality Disorder.

Mrs Upstairs calls Caitlin down to see her and sweeps her off into her sitting room/bunker. Caitlin looks terrified. I give her the thumbs up as she walks past me white-faced and shaking. I can't work out why this happens. I decide to give the job until after Christmas. After all, it is still a job, a job is a job, and I worry it will take me a while to find another one at this time of the year. Or at my age.

Tuesday 13th

I am dressed very flamboyantly today in my Arabian pants of many colours (you know the ones with the crotch down near the ankles), embroidered Indian top and Arabian slippers with toes that curl up and around. Usually, I don't wear my colourful clothes to work but with working weekends, I run out of time to do any washing.

Actually, I've put on so much weight with all hoovering through chocolates Davina and I do, I can no longer fit my small selection of boring work clothes. Besides, the place it so gloomy what with all the gloomy, miserable people I decide it can do with a bit of flamboyance.

The Dowager finds me in the Housekeepers' Hovel. She's about to say something but stops and gets a really weird look on her face. It's kind of like the expression you'd expect on an upper-class Boa Constrictor's face when they've just realised the rat they've swallowed is actually a sewer rat rather than say, a posher Manorial house attic rat. After several seconds of face contortions, she turns and walks out. It's only later, it occurs to me, she probably thinks because of the way I'm dressed, maybe I'm a 'Muzlin'.

Caitlin appears just after that.

'Are you all right?' I ask. She looks a bit freaked. I wonder what Mrs Upstairs said to her yesterday.

She nods, stops and clears her throat. I suddenly feel I'm not going to like what she's about to say.

'You know how I said you were to work the same hours as Davina while she was away. Well, it seems she meant permanently. Sorry. I guess I didn't hear it properly.' She looks upset.

I am a bit stunned. What? Can she do that? Cut my hours just like that without evening discussing it with me.

Yep, Mrs Upstairs word is law.

In my head, I chant 'only till Christmas, only till Christmas' as I work my way through my now reduced hours. There goes my extra two hundred pounds a month. This is not enough to live on. I am aggrieved. As Mrs Upstairs shuffles past me on her way from stuffing her face at the breakfast table to her bathroom upstairs to wrap her stomach in creams and clingfilm, I ask if I can talk to her.

'Not now,' she snaps barely looking at me.

Wednesday 14th

Today Caitlin gives me some more news I could well do without. Calis the Conservator is now to be my Supervisor. Like I need one. I am so shocked, there's nothing I can say. Apparently, Mrs Upstairs has decided things just aren't being done properly and we, Davina and myself, need to be properly supervised. I'm guessing the 'things that aren't being done properly' are those The Conservator has decided aren't being done properly because while I may be a bit of a rebel and inclined to help myself indiscriminately to her chocolates (surely, I am doing her a favour weight-wise), I actually do my job properly.

On the plus side, this means she is now a buffer between myself and Mrs Upstairs which can't be a bad thing.

I phone up Davina to share the good news. She's horrified. She also tells me she's taking all the holiday she's owed and is going to Thailand for 4 weeks and won't be back until the end of January.

I think I hate her.

Thursday 15th

I catch Mrs Upstairs mid coconut water and pomegranate juice gulp and ask point blank if she could explain what things weren't being cleaned properly. She splutters unattractively and sprays her white towelling dressing gown with pink spots.

She tells me I should discuss it with Calis. When I point out I would have discussed it with Calis if I'd known there was an issue in the first place so maybe it's really the lack of proper communication that's the real issue, she does some more of her facial contortions and stalks out.

Well, that was productive.

I go up to the office to talk to Ivo about my reduction in hours. His response? Housekeeping is nothing to do with him. I must talk to Mrs Upstairs (he calls her the Dowager Duchess and I try to remember to not call her Mrs Upstairs). No help there then.

Friday 16th

I begin to think Calis's promotion is more to do with Mrs Upstairs not being able to deal with me because I'm not subservient or obsequious enough. Who knows? I'm just making a wild guess because I know I have a tendency to answer her back.

I decide this promotion is good for The Conservator and her narcissism. I am pleased for her. She can't stand me but I can live with that if it means Mrs Upstairs no longer shouts at me because of her bath towel sizing issues and her exacting size and colour standards re lemons or her nutty need to piece together shattered glass shards into the shape of the vase they once were.

And to be fair, Calis has waited a long time for this promotion. I think since about 1985. At last, she can feel important and appreciated. It was probably hard for her, all those other Head housekeepers coming in over her. And the way she set about getting rid of them suggests she took it to heart. After all, I think her title of Conservator is really just a sort of ego boost for her since she is effectively Mrs Upstairs personal maid. I mean what else do you call someone who handwashes and irons all your clothes, does all your packing and unpacking, darns and mends (I kid you not), lays out your daily clothes, chooses your nightwear and so on?

Her lair, in which she hovers menacingly, has huge concrete tubs for handwashing and huge industrial washing machines for washing towels and linen. In the middle stands a long table beside which she hovers menacingly while shrouded in a miasma of steam and cigarette smoke while ironing the damp linen. Above her are wooden racks for drying the still damp but now crease free linen.

I do think it is a bit odd because there always seems to be linen and towels being washed and ironed yet Mrs Upstairs' bed linen and towels are changed only once a week. So, it seems it takes Calis a week to wash, dry and iron 2 sheets, 3 pillowcases and 3 towels?

Really?

Not terribly efficient then.

I've been told I must now knock before entering her lair as she's the 'supervisor' and I am merely a Housekeeper, probably with a small 'h'. I always leave the room gasping for air. I'm sure if I stay in there for too long, I will drown in the damp atmosphere. On the plus side, it's probably really good for my skin and any blocked pores I may have developed from all the dusting.

The conservator bit of her job seems to consist mostly of marching around the Manor with Moaning Morbid Murdo in tow, taking damp readings, setting traps for little insects and grumbling. Oh, and climbing unstable ladders to clean ancient light fittings.

I've asked several times about risk assessments, not because I actually care about them as I've completed more of them in my life than I want to think about but simply because I can. However, all I get in response are snorts of derisive laughter. Usually from the Conservator and sometimes from Ivo who gives me a pained smile.

So, this day, when I see Calis the Conservator perched on the top rung of an old wobbly wooden ladder while attempting to clean some ancient light fighting, I look up and, from the safety of the floor, ask if she's done a risk assessment for that job. I do this just to see the reaction. She snorts so furiously, the ladder wobbles, one leg slips a little on the polished floor and she nearly falls off but is saved by grabbing the curtain pelmet.

'I take it that's a No then,' I say rather smugly while she steadies herself. I note, with delight, she's gone an interesting shade of terrified.

I think I made my point.

Anyway, today working at the Manor is actually pleasant. Mrs Upstairs is going away for the weekend so she leaves at about 11 am. She's also scoffed her breakfast early so I get to clean up after her earlier than usual. And because she's going away, she hardly spends any time in the bathroom room. I do a little dance on one of the ancient silk carpets in the Portrait

Gallery (double the insult because I'm doing it in front of the ancestors) while wearing my outdoor clumpy boots after removing the slip-on plastic shoe covers we all have to wear while working indoors (have I mentioned these? No? Heaven forbid we walk some common dirt into her posh presence. We all look like a CSI). The gardeners all have to put them on over their clumpy work boots when they come instead to deliver the sticks for the fire or water and/or replace her always dying plants. See, even the plants can't handle too much time in her company.

Mrs Upstairs has explained to me earlier this morning, in the icy, precise voice she uses when addressing the slow-witted staff, how I must not touch the velvet curtain around her four-poster bed because it is very old and fragile. I apologise and say I hadn't realised I had touched them. She looks askance at my response and I wonder, now I have a supervisor should I perhaps direct my response to her in the first instance so she can convey it to Mrs Upstairs? I admit I struggle with the etiquette involved between Dowager Duchess and domestic servant. I do wonder, however, if the bed with its horsehair mattress and its velvet curtains is so old and fragile then really, surely, it's time she upgraded to a new Sealy Posturepedic?

I wonder if I can talk to Calis about the reduction in my working hours. The thought barely forms before I brush it away. Why bother? I sense Calis would rather cut her tongue out than help me.

Monday 19th

I am missing Davina. Calis the Conservator is in full narcissist swing. She doesn't seem to get that if she terrorises me out of this job, then it all falls on her shoulders especially in Davina's absence. Maybe she doesn't care. Maybe it's more important for her to get her own way and damn the consequences. Frankly, I'm feeling a bit over it all.

She instructs me to vacuum the carpet in the dining room because, as she points out, Mrs Upstairs is a messy eater (Seriously. Toddlers in high-chairs make less mess) and food has been ground into the ancient carpet. Indeed, I am always shocked at the mess Mrs Upstairs leaves. Clearly, no one thought to teach her any table manners. The dining room is very long, yet she manages to spread her bits of food far and wide.

I plug in the vacuum cleaner, turn on the generator (no, actually that's an exaggeration there is mains electricity but only just), flick the switch on the wall socket, pick up the metal bit you use to push the sucky bit around on the floor and get an electric shock intense enough to make me throw it across the room. Sparks fly, the vacuum cleaner goes phut and puffs of smoke billow, or possibly just waft, out. At the same time, the plug in the wall socket gives a loud bang, sparks and catches fire.

My fault? Don't think so but the way the Supervisor goes on about it, you'd think I'd been practising the dark arts or something in there. Is this a spell gone wrong? Maybe but not mine, though I wish I'd thought of it. When I point out all accidents must be recorded in the accident record book because is a legal requirement, she rolls her eyes.

Then when I ask for a risk assessment to be done, she rolls her eyes again, smirks and snorts derisively (not a pleasant sound) before calling out to Manfred, 'what does she think this place is?' before doing some more of that derisive laughter she's clearly perfected over the years.

'A workplace,' I suggest at which point she glares at me and goes back to skulking in her lair.

I wander around aimlessly singing an Antipodean Christmas Carol. 'It's a Summer Wonderland' and try not to think about ice cold Sauvignon Blanc, good friends and a barbie on the beach. This place can't feel less festive if it tried.

I am homesick.

Tuesday 20th

Mrs Upstairs slept in today which is mildly frustrating as it messes up my timings. I've worked out a schedule which allows me to be one step ahead of her so I can sometimes manage not to see her at all. I practise stealth and invisibility. I hang out in her office instead where I can use the Wi-Fi. Davina and I found the password underneath the telephone. As a spy, Mrs Upstairs leaves a lot to be desired.

I am a bit aggrieved to see she lit the fire the previous day. I mean she has heaters and frankly, I'm a bit over cleaning out fireplaces and making up fires. For a start, I have to use a specific bucket and shovel to sweep up the ashes. This is kept outside the back door, which means a trek along a couple of miles of corridor, there and back, and I'm sure burning all that wood is bad for the environment. Then I have to go to the Housekeepers' hovel by the kitchen to get the Financial Times and kindlers and carry them back along another mile or so through the obstacle course that is the Long Drawing Room (it is about time Mrs Upstairs had a car boot sale. I mean seriously if she sat in a different chair every night it will take a good 6 months to get through them all. Who needs that many chairs?).

I am missing Davina. I decide, therefore, in the interests of sanity, mine, to forgo the bucket and shovel trek, and just vacuum up the ashes instead. It is only when I got to the bottom, I realise the embers are still hot. I'm seriously hoping I haven't ruined this vacuum cleaner since I somehow allegedly destroyed the other one. Not sure it was my fault, I blame the ancient electrics. I hide this one in the linen cupboard upstairs.

I'm not worried about this vacuum cleaner for several reasons. I have a contingency plan. I know where I can get a replacement. In the cupboard by the shop downstairs next to the old kitchen, there is one exactly like it. It is used only in the summer but by this coming summer with the arrival of new summer staff and a new general manager (we are all looking forward to his arrival with eager anticipation because Ivo is truly a waste of space) no one will know one was ever there.

I can hide the current one in the vacuum cleaner graveyard; a bedroom in the East Wing is full of dead vacuum cleaners of all ages and types (Mrs Upstairs throws nothing away, I mean nothing. She has cupboards full of old shoes and clothes so beyond wearing even tramps will turn their noses up at them).

Anyway, I haven't forgiven her for not just cutting my hours but for not even having the good manners to discuss this with me.

Thursday 22nd

Mrs Upstairs tracks me down in the Portrait Gallery where I'm giving the ancestors a last bit of spit and polish before the Christmas break. She throws a bottle of window cleaner at me. Seriously, she lobs it at me with all the strength of a Southern Belle chucking insults to the slaves. It seems I left it on the window ledge in her office.

She is icy with rage.

I am speechless with horror.

Not sure I did leave it there (I suspect Calis is practising acts of sabotage) since I am now very careful with the cleaning products and where I leave them. Thankfully, she doesn't say anything else but flounces, in an ungainly, wobbly, creaky way from the room.

I spend the next 10 minutes spraying all the windows in the Long Gallery with the said window cleaner. We are not supposed to use window cleaner on these particular windows because they're all covered with a special film to keep the sun out. Window cleaner corrodes the film apparently.

Shame.

The bottle she chucked at me did hit me. I wonder if I can get her arrested for assault. This little fantasy fills a few pleasant moments during which time, I've got all the TV and radio news channels along with all the newspapers including the Financial Times along to witness her humiliation as she's ushered handcuffed into the back of a police car with her corsets creaking desperately.

Her word against mine. I have little doubt who would be believed.

Friday 23rd

Today is the last working day before Christmas. I'm feeling miserable and sorry for myself. I'm fed up with the miserable weather and miserable people and spoilt pampered Bohemian /Americans who think because they married into the aristocracy this somehow makes them better than anyone else. I am missing sunshine, cold wine, laughter and friends. I am missing a proper Christmas. My proper summer fun Christmas, not this dull, grey flat one.

Still, in the interests of harmony and good will, I take in some little bags of home-made chocolates and toffees.

Mrs Upstairs is on her way out the door to catch a flight to the US where she's visiting family and spending Christmas with her disgraced Ivory Smuggling Son. I give her a bag as she's getting ready to go. She's surprised (I can tell from the way she blinks repeatedly and very fast).

'Oh well, thank you,' she says, not particularly gracefully but she's not graceful so that's no surprise. 'I didn't get you anything,' she says, 'because you haven't worked for me for long enough.'

Ouch.

I go back inside to find The Conservator standing on the other side of the door, smirking. I give her a big beaming smile and hand over her bag of chocolates. She's taken them before she realises what I've given her.

'Oh, I don't do Christmas,' she says rudely thrusting them back at me, 'take them back.'

Rude cow. I ignore her and stalk off to the Hovel.

I later hear her repeating to Manfred Mrs Upstairs' response to my gift giving. She thinks it's hilarious. Though to be fair, Manfred did come to my defence. He likes my chocolates.

'That was a bit rude,' he says but it's not so much what he says as the way he says it. The Conservator is not happy. He should be rejoicing as is she. I wonder if he's feeling uncomfortable because lately, he has pretty much stopped looking at me and seems to avoid talking to me. Not sure why but as I'm always interrupting Calis the Callous moaning to him about me (never knew I was so interesting) I wonder if he's just sick of hearing about me. Doubt it, I suspect he's been turned. Along with the Morbidly Miserable Murdo.

I am cool but polite to him, though I did leave him some chocolates. True, there is a bit of me that hopes he'll feel bad for the way he's treated me so not entirely altruistic of me.

'Well, she won't be getting anything next year either,' she says snarkily, 'she's not liked so I doubt she'll be staying.'

Manfred asks her how she's going to manage without me. At which, point, The Conservator's narcissism makes her indiscreet. 'It's okay, I'm just waiting for Davina to come back then she'll be gone.'

JANUARY

Monday 9th

Okay, I've been ill for the last few days but the way The Conservator carries on, you'd think I'd done it on purpose with the sole intention of inconveniencing her because it means she's been really busy; really, really busy doing... well, not sure what, but she's been busy doing whatever it is. I only turn up today because I know Davina is still is away and whatever I am, I am responsible and try to do a good job even when it's one I'm now beginning to loathe.

I have cold sores around my mouth and nose and I'm coughing like a consumptive. Calis just snorts and tells me to keep away from her because she doesn't want to get what I've got since I look so awful.

Yep, that callous.

Mrs Upstairs is due back tomorrow. I hope she's had a nice time. I hope she's in a good mood. okay, I'm not looking forward to it. Morbidly Miserable Murdo has stopped talking to me again so I guess there's been a bit of back stabbing fest going on in my absence.

It is odd how Calis sticks like glue to him. They're always sitting outside in the garden, even when it's freezing, smoking fags and gripping. I'm wondering if she has a bit of thing for him. She treats her husband, Downtrodden, with a fair bit of off-handedness. I almost feel sorry for him until I remember the sniggering he along with her sons, Dimwitted and Docile, directed at me way back in the autumn. I'm not in the mood to be forgiving. I'm feeling isolated and a bit trapped. Seems in my unprotected state, I'm fair game for them. I haven't forgotten the comment I heard before Christmas either. I am biding my time.

Tuesday 10th

Mrs Upstairs arrives back in the early hours and has clearly been making the most of the Christmas fayre served up to her on her holiday. She definitely looks chubbier around the chops. I catch her slurping on her coconut and pomegranate juice this morning, which was disappointing. I thought she'd still be in bed.

'Good morning,' I say (I never use her title though I've been told by more than one member of staff that it's infra-dig not to. Not entirely sure what it means but I guess it's not polite. Who cares?) Did you have a lovely holiday?'

She looks positively astonished at my presumption in speaking to her without being spoken to first. Who am I to ask her about her holiday? She looks a weird mixture of shocked, pissed off and uncomfortable. I guess she doesn't know how to react when a servant engages with her as an equal. I mean, what the hell will happen to the class system.

She settles for having a dig at me because no lemon was left on her morning tray. I politely tell her,

I'll let Calis know thereby telling her it was Calis who did her tray without actually saying so. I'm keeping to my moral high ground of not playing the blame game though I really, really want to.

As I'm getting ready to leave after what feels like a never-ending morning, I witness the full extent of Calis the Conservator's narcissism and the full extent of Ivo the Idiot's fear of her. A researcher arrived just after New Year and he's been hanging about in the small dining room checking for some historical information in the Manor archives. I want desperately to snoop through these archives but I made the decision to keep my postgraduate history degrees to myself so I say nothing.

Ivo is telling me about the researcher (he has this propensity for long winded explanations about inconsequential things but yet always dashes off and away very quickly when it comes to talking about anything consequential) and how he's just going to pop his head around the door to say hello. Why he feels the need to tell me this, I have no idea and I'm fast getting close to the point of losing the will to live while I assure his desperate ego the researcher would probably really like, in fact probably really love to see him. Did I overdo it. No, I see the smug look on his face and guess I pitched it just right.

At this moment, Calis appears at the doorway where she stands and glares at him. He then quickly says, 'oh only if that's okay with you Calis?' Calis smiles/smirks her agreement and watches him walk away with a smugness that's actually unnerving to witness.

Bloody hell, I think as I walk away. He's the general manager and she's just a supervisor. I know that's not true. He's the general manager and she's the supreme ruler. Never imagine for a minute it's anything else. I know now how alone and defenceless I am stuck in the mire of Calis The Callous Conservator's private fiefdom with only Ivo the Idiot for support.

Wednesday 11th

There's no water. Something seems to have happened to it so Mrs Upstairs can't run her bath and, oh dear, I can't wash her dishes or clean her bathroom. She's raging through the Manor in her pink juice splattered dressing gown (she probably doesn't know where the clean ones are kept since it's our job to remove and replace them on laundry day, usually Monday when we also put out her clean night dress and change her sheets).

Then Manfred has to break the news there's no water to make her tea or indeed to poach her eggs for breakfast. I imagine she's hyperventilating at the mere thought of not getting fed. There are plenty of chocolates around. I'm sure she won't go hungry.

She orders Miserable Murdo off to investigate which means he has a trek through a forest to the water source. Murdo is not happy (oh, there's a surprise) and leaves muttering miserably under his breath. In the meantime, Ivo is harried to work early so he can sort out a plumber to find out what's gone wrong because heaven forbid, she might have to spend a day being unwashed. How common.

Manfred, I notice is huddled by the fridge looking anxious. I know this is where he keeps his beer supply but always pretend I don't. Not my business but I sense because this time in the morning is usually when it's quiet in the kitchen, whereas today it's like Edinburgh railway station, so it's likely he can't have his calming morning tipple. Or perhaps Mrs Upstairs screeching like a fire alarm is giving him a headache. It has me.

When Murdo returns miserably, he reports the water flow from the Estate Reservoir has been blocked and diverted. Possibly deliberately. This fills me with joy. Not sure why but there's something subversive about it that appeals to me. Seems her water comes from the Estate controlled part of the Estate. Oh, looks very like sabotage. Young Duke's revenge. I can see Miserable Murdo and Manfred think so too but they're not about to say so in front of me. I am so not in their clique.

Ivo gets her hooked up to the mains water supply, which is really annoying for Mrs Upstairs because now she'll have to pay for her water like the rest of the population. Shame.

Weird how these people who can afford to pay for these things who have shed loads of dosh, think they're entitled to everything for free: from Range Rovers to water.

Thursday 12th

I stay out of her way today as I hear she hasn't got over, or to the bottom of, the water supply sabotage yet. I've heard her shouting for me (how common) but I know the concealed doors in the Library, Portrait Gallery, Long Gallery and Drawing Rooms (plural) are so I utilise them to make my escape. I guess they were originally installed to allow the servants to move around the Manor without being seen and thereby, saving their masters/mistresses the inconvenience of acknowledging the household is run by people and not fairies.

Unfortunately, as I'm getting ready to leave at the end of my shift, I don't escape early enough. I'm on my way out the door when Miserable Murdo calls me back. Mrs Upstairs has just been on the phone to tell him to send me to her sitting room/office/bunker. I feel my stomach fall. This can only be bad.

When I knock on the door, she shouts at me to come in. Oh, am I about to witness her 'going mad' at long last? Seems so. Apparently, I used the wrong paper when making up her fire.

Seriously the wrong paper!

She keeps demanding to know why, why, why, I've done this but won't shut up for long enough to let me speak so I can explain it wasn't done on purpose. Where I come from the paper is paper is paper. I wonder if she and Calis attended the same course on staff relations, which is all about intimidation, shouting and not letting anyone else get a word in edgewise. She's incandescent with rage. On other occasions, I would find this interesting to observe but this seems a bit dangerously over the top. I keep my eye on the pokayer and wait until she runs out of steam, say sorry and stalk out quickly. I only just manage not to run.

Seriously.

Over this.

Crazy, mad, disagreeable woman. Only the Financial Times to be used in her fire. Not sure how she can tell it isn't since I can't imagine she's so delicate and sensitive she can tell the difference while it's burning.

Friday 13th

I leave bits of paper with made-up occult signs on them in the Housekeepers' cupboard for Calis to find. She has given me some odd looks lately. Unfortunately, I suspect she's too confident in her narcissism to be undermined by a mere mortal such as myself. Even one who may be practising the dark arts.

Before breakfast, I hide out in Mrs Upstairs office while she's faffing about in her bathroom, to use her Wi-Fi and computer to job search. I figure I have about an hour.

Later, when I'm in the flower room pretending to tidy up after the gardeners, Mrs Upstairs catches me and spits venom because I've left the wrong sized lemon on her tray. Again! Not only that, but I haven't polished her taps properly. I think she's just enjoying having a go at me. Or maybe this is payback for my daring to be presumptuous and speak to her as an equal.

This lemon thing seems way over the top. I suggest calmly she have a word with Tescos since I don't have any control over what size or colour of lemons they put in their organic pack. I also calmly point out this is how you can tell for real they are organic. If they are of a uniform size and colour, chances are they've been artificially cultivated. I say this as if I'm giving her some crucial and important information. She gives me such a cold stare back, I'm actually a bit freaked.

'Where are you from again?' she finally asks. When I tell her, she stares at me for a bit longer before saying, 'well, I guess that explains it.' I'm almost tempted to point out saying 'I guess' is a bit common but after the fire paper rant and now the lemon lament, I'm a feeling a bit circumspect. I wonder if I've underestimated her in the past. However, I am also beginning to suspect Calis has been stirring it up since they seem to spend a lot of time in her pink dressing room muttering together. The Conservator's patronising smirks seem to have increased in intensity and smugness so I feel something is afoot. And no doubt it's going to be unpleasant for me.

The Conservator finds me and asks why I haven't made up the guest room as Mrs Upstairs has a guest arriving in less than an hour. I point out it would have been useful to have had this information say, yesterday. I absolutely did not know any guest was due.

'I told you yesterday,' she lies (see; as easily as she breathes). She's covering her arse in case I complain about her not giving me the information.

Saturday 14th – Sunday 15th

I spend the weekend job hunting. I've sent off more Resumes and cover letters than I thought possible. I've applied for anything from Private Investigator to Blog writer.

Monday 16th

Mrs Upstairs guest is to leave after breakfast. I go into his room flick the light switch only to find the lights don't work so I strip the bed in darkness, collect the towels and put the chocolates he didn't eat back in the box in the Chinese cabinet. I let Miserable Moaning Murdo know the lights in that room don't work. He ignores me and disappears. I ask Manfred to help because I suspect I'll be the scapegoat for this. Luckily, he shows me where the fuse box is and I untrip the trip switch. The guest, however, has already complained to Mrs Upstairs who wobbles and creaks her way down to the room to investigate.

I'm in the Short Drawing Room making up the fire (with the Financial Times) and he's in there sitting on an ancient but wobbly chair (this chair is so fragile, I'm not allowed to dust it. Wonder how she feels about him sitting in it) chatting to me about a holiday he's just had in Queenstown and waxing lyrical about the beauty of New Zealand and the friendliness of New Zealanders.

Mrs Upstairs enters and glares frostily at me for making free with her guests and talking with them. She turns and smiles at him and says she's sorted out the lights and how sorry she is for him being so inconvenienced. Bloody hell. That's a bit low, taking the credit like that. I transgress the Dowager Duchess and dim-witted domestic servant boundary to tell him the trip switch had tripped so all I had to do was 'untrip it' and sorry for the inconvenience. Perhaps I should show him where it is in case it happens again the next time he stays.

I feel Mrs Upstairs' eyes boring in the back of my head. I think she may be snorting rockets but I don't want to look.

He gives me a £20 tip and tells me how it was a such a pleasure chatting with me. I resist looking at Mrs Upstairs. I rub salt into the wound by telling him the next time he heads Down Under, to let me know and I'll put him in touch with some friends who will be only too pleased to show him around. He thanks me profusely.

Mrs Upstairs stares at me rigid with rage.

She's driving him to the airport and as they go off, I hear him downstairs telling her what a nice person I am and how he had such a lovely chat with me. Hope that's really got up her nose. I do another jig in my outdoor boots on her ancient, handwoven silk carpet and sit for a few seconds in the fragile chair. It's very uncomfortable but I'm making a point if only to myself.

She's back before I leave, and snorting fire. She's clearly been fuming all the way back. It transpires I must NEVER, NEVER strip the guests' beds and remove their towels until the next day in case their travel plans are messed up and they have to return for another night.

'Well, shame I wasn't told this yesterday,' I now decide this is a comment worth repeating. Mainly because it's true. I'm getting fed up being told off for not doing or doing something I should or shouldn't when no one has given me the information. This is seriously getting up my nose.

Calis comes in and demands to know what's happened to the chocolates left beside his bed because she checked this morning and he hadn't eaten any. I tell her coldly how I'd put them back in the box (not lying. Not feeling well enough to eat chocolates). Calis smirks and says we never do that. She is implying I'm lying. I tell Mrs Upstairs I think it probably a wise move considering the problem they have with mice. I can tell I've hit a nerve. Neither of them says a word. Enjoying my moment on the moral high ground, I stalk off. Not sure I can deal any longer with this mind-numbing surfeit of pettiness. Not sure either why they seem to have ganged up on me. I suspect it's because Davina is due back and I am to be got rid of.

Tuesday 17th

This morning when I am in the kitchen washing her breakfast dishes (I leave the silverware in the water for as long as I can but sadly none has come unglued yet), Calis comes in, starts polishing some silver (she does this when she's pretending to work because polishing silver is so difficult and time-consuming... not) and starts bantering with Manfred. I have my back to her but sense it's somehow for my benefit. Or maybe bantering simply isn't in her nature. There's something forced and jolly about her tone.

When I turn around and start putting the cutlery on the tray to carry through to the Dining Room (heaven forbid I carry it in my hand because, in my dim-witted servant way, I might drop it), she laughs (nope, pretty sure I heard nothing remotely amusing) and says, 'you haven't forgotten our curry night, our monthly curry night have you, Manfred?' At this point, Morbid Murdo walks in.

'Come on guys, how about this Friday?'

I quickly take the cutlery tray into the Dining Room before she catches me smiling. Was that for my benefit? Probably. I think she is more dangerous than I realise because I'm finally getting the strength of her possessiveness and jealousy. Miserable Murdo and Manfred are her friends. I get the message. I must keep my distance from them. Not that it matters, I think she's successfully turned them anyway.

I remind myself I'm a grown up but it doesn't feel like it. I feel in the space of a few months I've reverted to a powerless teenager. It's not a nice feeling. I'm not sure how to deal with it. Odd to think only a few months ago, I was the boss. I like to think I was better than Mrs Upstairs.

Wednesday 18th

Today, after threatening it to myself, in my mind for weeks, I feel I am truly coming to the end of my tether. My gut feeling is I'm bordering on walking out but I make a promise to myself, I will stay for as long as I can stand it and then some. After that I will leave because then I will know, I've done my best.

After breakfast, I'm rushing to get her dishes done and clean the Dining Room (bearing in mind I am entirely on my own. Doing the work of two in half the time. This is seriously getting to me) when Mrs Upstairs orders me to clean the outside of the window in the dining room. The one where the birds' feeding table is situated. Birds and squirrels are messy eaters. This particular window is always covered with shit of some description.

I point out doing this means hanging out over a drop of several hundred feet down to the river below. And besides, it's snowing outside. And I've still got all my other jobs to complete.

'Well, perhaps you shouldn't dawdle so much. And you will do as I say without daring to presume you can speak to me like that,' she says nastily, as she wobbles and creaks away. It's then I see Calis hovering in the dim room, she's counting the cutlery (in case I'm tempted to steal any) while smiling to herself.

I tell her I haven't finished in here and if I do the window, then I won't have time to do the bathroom either. She shrugs, smirks and turns away saying, 'oh well that's your problem.' I remind her, she is my supervisor and ask if it isn't part of her job to intervene on my behalf with the Dowager Duchess.

She shrugs and tells me if I'm unhappy with the way things are run, then I should have a word with her. Fat chance. I still haven't had a chance to speak to her about the arbitrary reduction in my hours.

I am depressed. I go into the kitchen, uncork an opened bottle of wine on the sideboard and glug down a couple of mouthfuls of Mrs Upstairs expensive claret. It's not even 9.30 in the morning yet. This is not good.

It's at this point I realise the extent to which all this nagging and pettiness has begun to erode my self-confidence. So much for a quiet stress-free job I can leave at the end of the day and not think about until the next morning.

I go upstairs to the office eerie seeking succour. Huh, I have more chance of discovering gold in the gutter at the end of the driveway.

'I need to talk to you,' I tell Ivo the Idiot.

He gets a slightly panicked look which doesn't bode well. He's also about to leave this job to move on to another one in greener and possibly calmer pastures so I guess he doesn't really care any more.

'It's about Calis...' I start but before I can finish my sentence, he brutally tells me not to bother because 'Housekeeping' is not his domain.

When I ask him who I can talk to about it, he shrugs his shoulders and suggests Calis in the first instance and Mrs Upstairs in the second. No help there then, especially as my issue is with both of them, I feel confident talking to either will be a complete waste of time.

I am, I realise, in this situation entirely on my own. No back up. No support. No understanding. Down there on the front line. Alone. It's not a good thought.

I miss Davina. I wish she'd come back.

Thursday 19th

This morning I tell Calis the Callous I have to leave early for a hospital appointment (true, not lying though as an excuse it has a lot going for it). She rolls her eyes and snorts derisively. Not sure I can deal with so such a surfeit of sympathy.

Later, as I'm about to leave I overhear her telling Manfred as he's on his way to the supermarket, Mrs Upstairs has told him to follow me to make sure I am really going to the hospital. I am blind-sided by this. I walk to my car and realise, despite reminding myself not to underestimate The Conservator, I have indeed done just that. The Conservator and Mrs Upstairs, both. I remember the removal of Rochelle and Elissa. This is not good. It's also, however, a bit of a relief. Too many narcissists, egotists, passive/aggressive, misery guts, buck passers and alcoholics for my liking. This is not a healthy environment.

As I drive away in my car, I wait at the end of the drive for Manfred to catch up with me. Driving is not something he is either confident or good at. I keep slowing down so he doesn't lose me.

I wave to him, as I go off the roundabout towards the hospital. He waves back before realising what he's done then looks shocked as he goes around the roundabout again. As I'm waiting for the traffic lights to turn green, I see him go around a couple more times.

I almost feel sorry for him until I remember he was sent to spy on me. Not a good feeling.

I can't work out if they are all thick enough to imagine I'm not aware of their machinations because they are certainly not at all discreet, or whether they actually believe I'm so dim, I'm unaware.

Either is insulting.

I remind myself, I'm worth more than this. It's good to remind myself.

Friday 20th

I spend as little time as possible in the kitchen today. I am disappointed in Manfred. I thought we had a kind of friendship but it's clearer by the day I'm mistaken. He won't look at me now and seems uncomfortable when I appear. He keeps his back to me most of the time and pretends he's busy and lost in thought if ever I attempt talk to him.

I wait until I catch his eye. I make this difficult for him to avoid as I pretty much stand directly in front of him. He shuffles for a bit, looks desperately over to the corner where he keeps his beer stash before taking a breath and grimacing at me. I could be underestimating him. Perhaps it was a smile but I'm not in the mood to accept it. I'm almost enjoying my aggrievement. I ask him bluntly if he had a nice afternoon at the supermarket. Yes, I know I'm being provocative but it's better than being passive. His eyes do a few crazy exercises before he decides to pretend he didn't hear me and turns his radio up. I wash Mrs Upstairs breakfast dishes to the sound of David Bowie singing 'Heroes' which is inspiring until I remember he's dead and I go back to feeling depressed.

As I leave, I gently tell Manfred I drove really slowly yesterday so he wouldn't lose me. He doesn't answer but keeps his head down while vigorously beating some eggs to death. I leave early and don't bother to clock out. Seriously pissed off now.

Monday 24th

Today I come to a decision. Halfway through this morning before I finish making Mrs Upstairs bed and before I've made up any of the fires, I go up to the office to tell Caitlin I'm ill and won't be in for the rest of the week. Davina will be back at the end of the week. Let's see how Mrs Upstairs and Calis The Callous get on in the meantime. Not that I care. It is not my intention to return. Ever.

It's snowing, it's freezing but the sky is blue and the sun is shining. As I walk down towards the impressive, black wrought iron gates, I suddenly feel a huge sense of relief. This lovely Manor is not so lovely. It is, it turns out a dark, dark place. I feel a bit sad about the way it all turned out especially when I remember how excited I had been when I first walked over the drawbridge way back in the early summer; I recall all the light-hearted gossiping summer staff, the friendly chats, the ghost in the garden. A lifetime ago.

Then I remind myself, it only seems good in retrospect and then only because it got so bad. It's a bit like being in an abusive relationship. It creeps up on you little by little. Mrs Upstairs needs to get a life and so does Calis the Cruel Conservator and Lady's Maid. Seriously a life. It's no life in there, living like they do. It's some kind of weird prison, a gilded cage and they have become institutionalised.

Good experience but not one I'll be repeating in a hurry or indeed if ever. I am worth so much more than this.

I decide, however, to have the last word. When I get home, I email Ivo the Idiot a copy of the details defining an Employer's Duty of Care. Apparently, these requirements under an employer's duty of care are wide-ranging and may manifest themselves in many different ways, such as:

- Clearly defining jobs and undertaking risk assessments
- Ensuring a safe work environment
- Providing adequate training and feedback on performance
- Ensuring staff do not work excessive hours
- Providing areas for rest and relaxation
- Protecting staff from bullying or harassment, either from colleagues or third parties

- Protecting staff from discrimination
- Providing communication channels for employees to raise concerns
- Consulting employees on issues which concern them.

I highlight where I feel he, Cauldon Manor and Mrs Upstairs fail, which oddly enough seems to be in all of them.

I hope they enjoy reading them.

I discover I am right. Plots and plans are indeed afoot to dispense with my services. Well, I'm saying it like that because basically, I am to be sacked. Not sure of the grounds but I suspect it doesn't matter to these kinds of people. Mrs Upstairs and her acolytes seem to think they can do anything they like because somehow, they are above the law. Or above any kind of humanity. I think it has something to do with living in the 19th Century. And I'm sure Calis had made up something really nasty about me.

No doubt, Ivo the Idiot was fully complicit as well. He keeps texting me to ask for a meeting. I just text back to say I'm too ill to move. After a week or so of this, I change the message to 'No, can't be bothered'. Like I'm really stupid enough to go.

I spend a morning after my departure (they are, of course, expecting me to turn up for work when I've recovered because I keep saying I will. I am seriously not dim-witted) organising a sick note with my doctor, who diagnoses me with depression, perusing Cauldron Manor review sites and reading, with a great deal of perverse enjoyment, all the worse reviews about the it. Here I stumbled across an advert for my job. Not surprised but a little bemused by it all. Says a lot about the class system and the arrogance of those who think because they have a title, they are above everyone else, and the law. I wonder if it would have been different if

I'd insisted they use my title, true not an aristocratic one, an academic one but a title nonetheless and one I earned rather than just given. Would they have perhaps perceived me in a different light? No, probably not.

It was both ignorant and arrogant of Mrs Upstairs to simply view and define me entirely by the job I did for her. Odd too, how she makes such a fuss about everything needing to be done to her exacting standards, and obviously this is extremely important (possibly on the edge of irrationally important. Or even insanity) to her but yet at the same time, not important enough for her to pay those she employs to do this job either a liveable wage or treat them with any kind of respect.

I now work in an Eco Village in Nepal. I appreciate the simplicity, the lack of clutter, the humility and humanity of my co-workers and those whom we live amongst. Especially after my experience at the Manor working with those sad people slaving away for a mean-spirited woman who, for some reason, believes marrying a bloke who has a title and who leaves her his stately pile makes her somehow better than anyone else. I think she proved, she's not.

And, as I eventually discover, it ultimately didn't serve her well in the end.

One morning, I'm sitting savouring my morning chai enjoying the feel of the sun on my face while listening to the chatter of school children, I find an old Scottish newspaper left behind by one of the other volunteers. It's several weeks old but as I'm scanning through the name Cauldron Manor suddenly catches my eye. I find myself reading a report about the how the Dowager Duchess's body has found at the bottom of the stone steps leading down to the dungeons. It's reported as an accidental death. It would seem she simply slipped and fell. A sad tragedy.

I ponder this for a while. A slip and fall or a push and fall. How would it be possible to tell such a thing. A slip and fall or a push and fall, almost amounts to the same thing. I know those stone steps very well. I should do since I dusted and brushed them often enough in the summer. The middle of each step is concave and worn smooth with centuries of use. True, there is a thick rope strung along on both sides of the wall on either side of the steps for scaredy cats like me, who tended to clutch on to them for dear life (dear life?) because I was terrified of slipping and falling. Yet, I watched the others trip up and down them without a thought or care mostly because they were used to them as was the Dowager. Maybe she did simply stumble and fall. Who knows? I guess no one ever will.

Later, several weeks later, I am surprised by a text I get from Davina – I'm not surprised at getting one from her, we had stayed in touch so she could remind me daily about the doings in the Manor house so I could continue to feel relieved and confident I'd made the right move – but rather I was surprised by the contents of the text. I can tell from the lack of punctuation, she's shocked. It takes me a while to decipher it because not only is there no punctuation, all the words have run together without a space between.

Then I see what she's messaged me.

Big news. Reporters were camped out in front of the Manor and the current Duke had been arrested for getting his Gamekeepers to fire off shotguns over their heads to get them to move on.

It was deliberate. Her death.

It turns out, someone, who remains nameless, has been arrested for pushing her, the Dowager, her Mrs Upstairs down the steps.

It takes me a while to get to access to a computer so it was a couple of days before I got to read about it.

Davina was right. It's big news and all over the papers, all over the country, all over the world, both print and digital ones. I wonder how she feels about that, the Dowager? Famous now and not just because of a family squabble or maybe it is just a family squabble. One that got out of hand?

Bruising on her back, which didn't show up immediately, revealed she'd been pushed with something circular. It was the undertakers who'd spotted it and they informed the police who then organised for a full forensic post-mortem to be carried out. As a result if was discovered she'd also been hit on the head with the ubiquitous blunt object because it made a mark unlike anything the steps would have made. Hit then pushed.

Not sure how I feel about this but while I'm shocked at such an ending for her, there is also a part of me that's a little disturbed. Such a pointless life and such a pointless way to die. Who was responsible? The papers give very little away.

As I sit back and sip my spiced chai, I shudder and wonder at the depth of feeling behind that push. The chances of it being an accident are minimal. You don't shove someone down those hard stone steep steps and even in your wildest dreams, ever imagine they'd survive. What was behind it? Hatred or anger? Difficult to know.

I text Davina to ask who had been arrested.

I wait for days before she finally gets back to me. The whole village has been inundated with reporters and TV crews so now everyone is a star revelling in their fifteen minutes of fame. The Dowager is almost a side story. Oh dear, pushed aside for the common folk's views. In death, she's been rendered almost inconsequential. It's a story about what happened to her, not a story about her. She's become significant now.

Yes, I text Davina, but who have the police arrested? I follow with several question marks so she gets how I really want to know. When she finally answers me, I'm stunned. But after a while, when I've thought about it, perhaps it's not so surprising after all. I suppose in the scheme of things, it was the most likely person which goes to prove, everyone has a breaking point somewhere.

Maybe it all comes down to karma. Hers, not mine.

THE END

Printed in Great
Britain
by Amazon